CONTENTS

ANNEXES

A. Sample Template for Terms of Engagement
B. Sample Template for Report
C. HMRC Business Income Manual – Schedule of Contents
D. Stock Valuations for Income Tax Purposes (HMRC Tax Bulletin May 1993)
E. Short Rotation Coppice (BIM 55120)
F. Treatment of the Single Payment (HMRC Tax Bulletin June 2005)
G. Arable Area Payments (HMRC Tax Bulletin February 1994)
H. The Times at which Animal Grants/Subsidies Should be Recognised for Tax Purposes (HMRC Tax Bulletin December 1994)
I. BSE and Farm Stocktaking Valuations (HMRC Press Release – 29th April 1996)
J. The Herd Basis – Extract from HMRC Help Sheet 224
K. Statement of Auditing Standards 520 – Using the Work of an Expert
L. Schedule of HMRC Guidance, Statutes, Cases and Accountancy Guidance

1. INTRODUCTION

1.1 General

1.1.1 Stocktaking is part of proper accounting under the accruals approach so that expenditure is matched against the income to which it relates. While this may be used for management purposes, it is more often met in practice for accounts for Income Tax or Corporation Tax purposes. This paper focuses on that need.

1.1.2 As the stocktaking forms an integral part of the taxpayer's annual accounts, it is of paramount importance that the valuer and accountant liaise so that the valuer's work on stocktaking is integrated with the accountant's work of preparing the accounts to ensure that:

- the approach of both is consistent
- all necessary matters are considered
- items are neither duplicated nor omitted.

1.1.3 Under the UK's self assessment regime the taxpayer has a duty of compliance and HMRC expects accounts to be correct. Errors in the accounts that are attributable to the stocktaking valuation may bring a financial penalty which the taxpayer may look to the valuer to recompense.

1.1.4 By implication, the professional advisers who assist in the preparation of the accounts will have part of that duty of compliance delegated to them. It is important for the protection of the professionals involved that the stocktaking and other judgments comply with HMRC's published guidance. When estimates and judgements are made, these need to be disclosed if they do not follow the accepted practice set out in such publications.

1.1.5 HMRC's general guidance on stocktaking is given in its Business Income Manual – a schedule of relevant contents is included here at Annexe C. At BIM33115, it recognises two bases of valuation (and only these two) as valid for stocktaking:

- the lower of cost or net realisable value which is the basis that will generally be familiar for agricultural stocktaking and is reviewed in Chapter 2 of this paper.
- "mark to market" which is essentially a market value approach required for valuations governed by International Financial Reporting Standards and reviewed in Chapter 4 of this paper. Not only is this basis occasionally met by agricultural valuers, usually where the client is a publicly quoted company, but there is increasing pressure from accounting standard setters for its principle to be applied more widely. However, HMRC advises that "Its use is not currently appropriate for agricultural produce" (Business Income Manual (BIM) 33160).

1.1.6 HMRC's specific guidance on farm stocktakings was last prepared as the then Inland Revenue's Business Economic Note 19 (BEN 19) of 1993. This has on occasion, as required, been supplemented by other announcements reproduced as Annexes to this paper. The text of BEN 19 now appears in the Business Income Manual at BIM 55410 and has also been published as HMRC Self Assessment Help Sheet IR232 (without its paragraph numbers). For familiarity and ease, this guidance is still referred to as BEN 19 and its paragraph numbers are used in this paper.

1.1.7 Where the principles set out in BEN 19 have not been followed, those departures need to be carefully justified. Undervaluing is as dangerous as overvaluing and a consistent basis must be adopted at all times. These notes endeavour to cover the major issues so that they can be properly considered in practice by the valuer and the accountant.

1.1.8   While there is still very little use in the United Kingdom of the alternative mark to-market basis for agricultural stocktakings, the growing pressure for its use under International Accounting Standards means that it is considered in Chapter 4. Not only does it apply under EU legislation to publicly quoted companies (and available for other that wish to adopt it) but, at the time of writing, the question of extending a version of as good accounting practice for the largest faming businesses is under review. Within farm stocktaking, this approach is only applied to growing and harvested crops an livestock, not to consumables. It is not applied to stocktaking for any other production business.

1.1.9   Separate accounting rules apply where there are long term contracts by which value is brought into the profit and loss account rather than deferred. These are considered in Chapter 5.

1.1.10 While the law expects accounts prepared for tax purposes to follow good accounting practice, this paper considers two points where statute overrides that an adjustments have to be made in preparing the tax return:
  – the substitution of capital allowances for depreciation which require adjustments to be made to cost-based stocktaking valuations in the tax computation which requires the valuer to report the appropriate element. This is considered in the paragraphs starting at 3.3.14.
  – the option given by the Herd Basis for farmers to elect that production animal should be treated in manner more akin to capital rather than trading stock. This is reviewed in Chapter 6.

1.1.11 Consistency in accounting policies is of great importance and any attempt to deviate from a consistent approach should only be undertaken with the agreement of the accountant.

1.2   Professional Standards

1.2.1   A farm stocktaking is a task to be undertaken professionally by an agricultural valuer under the professional standards of the CAAV's bylaws and who is encouraged:
  – to record his instructions and terms of engagement in writing
  – seek out, test and record relevant evidence
  – report clearly to the client with assumptions stated.
This paper offers guidance to assist valuers with the issues and problems that may be met. Its final sections consider the issues of instructions and reporting together with the interaction with valuation standards and practices. These are covered in Chapters 7 and 8

1.2.2   These matters are also covered by the valuation standards of which the main ones likely to be met by valuers in the United Kingdom are:
  – the RICS Valuation – Professional Standards (the Red Book – currently the 2012 edition) which now applies the valuation standards prepared by the International Valuation Standards Council (see below) but sets out rules or practice;
  – TEGoVA's European Valuation Standards (the Blue Book) prepared for valuations of real property but with valuation standards setting out definition and covering the valuation process and reporting;

– the International Valuation Standards (the White Book) which are now applied to RICS members through the Red Book.

1.2.3   **RICS Regulation** – For all members of the RICS and IRRV (and so most members of the CAAV), the Red Book applies to stocktaking save where the work is in the course of negotiations or potential litigation.

1.2.4   Where the stocktaking is to be prepared by an RICS member or an RICS regulated firm, then not only will the RICS expect the stocktaking to comply with the "Red Book" but also that the valuation be signed off by a valuer registered under the RICS Valuer Registration Scheme. The issues arising are discussed in Chapter 8 below.

2. BASIC PRINCIPLES OF STOCKTAKING

2.1   General

2.1.1   The essential expectation of accounts is that they give a true and fair view of the business' profits and losses in the relevant period.

2.1.2   Statute law requires that the profits of a business should be computed in accordance with generally accepted accounting practice (s.42, Finance Act 1998 as amended by s.103, Finance Act 2002). That practice is defined to mean generally accepted accounting practice with respect to accounts of UK companies that are intended to give a true and fair view (s.80, Finance Act 2005 formerly s.836A, Income and Corporation Taxes Act 1988). This means that HMRC's expectations of accounts are likely to change should approved accounting practices change. Thus, if accounting practices changed to recognise a mark-to-market approach for some agricultural stocktakings, HMRC would expect that to be followed though it would not directly override statute law on the assessment of taxation.

2.1.3   In arriving at that "true and fair view" of the profits or losses, a fundamental point is that the accounts require a valuation of stocks that have not been sold as at the balance sheet date. These may be goods that have been bought but not used by that date or (as with harvested crops) produce that is in store but not sold. In a farming context stocks will also include expenditure and work that has been committed to production to result in sales in the coming year (or even later periods). That value needs to be carried forward against those future sales.

2.1.4   Stocktakings are to be prepared according to normal accounting principles (save insofar as the law directs). The relevant guidance is in Statements of Standard Accounting Practice (SSAP) Numbers 2 and 9 issued by the Accounting Standards Board:
  – SSAP 2 introduces the concepts of accounting on an accruals basis and on a prudent basis.
  – SSAP 9 expects stocks to be carried forward from year to year at the lower of cost and net realisable value.

2.1.5   The requirements may be summarised. The valuation to be included in the accounts should:
  – reflect the correct application of the principles of normal accountancy
  – rely on a method which pays sufficient regard to the facts
  – not be contrary to tax law
  – be consistent from year to year.

2.1.6   Thus, it may, on occasion, be possible for other approaches to be used where these produce a true and fair view for the accounts. Thus, the decision in *Johnston Britannia Airways Ltd* said:
  'Which of the three ways in which the attribution of cost to a period or periods of accounting is adopted is, in my view, essentially a matter of accountancy judgement, and I am quite unable to detect any legal basis for excluding any of them.'
However the valuer should have clear instructions before adopting any basis other than the lower of cost or net realisable value. Whichever basis is adopted, it should then be followed consistently.

2.1.7   Those accounts may then need to be adjusted in the tax computation necessary for the tax return. This is discussed in context of any element of depreciation in a cost-based stocktaking in the paragraphs starting with 3.3.14 and also in the review of the Herd Basis in Chapter 6.

2.2   Conventional Application of a Cost Basis in the United Kingdom

2.2.1   British case law and practice has developed on the basis that stocks are assessed on the basis of the lower of cost or net realisable value, the principle followed through in BEN 19. This reflects a prudent assessment of the business' exposure to the costs that it has incurred rather than bringing unrealised profits forward as a consequence of adopting the alternative mark-to-market approach.

2.2.2   HMRC notes that mark-to-market:
> "… is only appropriate where there is a liquid market in the stock, so that the value could be realised easily. It is currently used by financial institutions and commodities dealers."

It says expressly at BIM 33160 "Its use is not currently appropriate for agricultural produce" and comments further at BIM 31027:
> "IAS41 prescribes the accounting treatment related to agricultural activity. At present the Inland Revenue do not consider that its use is within generally accepted accounting practice as defined in ICTA88/S836A. If accounts are prepared in accordance with IAS41 and tax computation adjustments are made to bring the stock valuation figures to SSAP9 figures this is acceptable for tax purposes."

The practical effect of that statement is unclear for those companies that are required by EU law to follow International Financial Reporting Standards (IFRS).

2.2.3   The cost approach was applied as a matter of common law in *Whimster and Co v CIR* in 1925:
> "…the ordinary principles of commercial accounting require that in the profit and loss account of a merchant's or manufacturer's business the values of the stock in trade at the beginning and at the end of the period covered by the account should be entered at cost or market price, whichever is the lower; although there is nothing about this in the taxing statutes."

CIR v Cock Russell & Co later refined market value to be net realisable value

2.2.4   This principle was affirmed by the 1993 case of *Gallagher v Jones* (also in *Threlfall v Jones*) in which Lord Nolan said
> "Mr Glick QC for the Crown submitted that there is a well-established precedent for such a disallowance in the accountancy practice whereby unsold stock-in-trade is brought into account at the beginning and at the end of the period at the lower of cost or market value, a practice recognised and approved for tax purposes as long ago as 1925 in *Whimster & Co v CIR 12TC813*. The effect of this practice, said Mr Glick, is to disallow the deduction of the trader's expenditure on the unsold stock (or so much of it as is represented by the market value, if lower) and carry it forward to be set against the price for which the stock is ultimately sold. That is certainly one way of describing the effect of the practice, and comes close to the language of Lord Reid in *Ostime v Duple Motor Bodies Ltd [1961] 39TC537 1WLR739* at page 754, where speaking of stock-in-trade and work-in-progress, he said:
>> 'So the question is not what expenditure it is proper to leave in the account as attributable to goods sold during the year, but what expenditure it is proper, in effect, to exclude from the account by setting against it a figure representing stock-in-trade and work in progress.'"

2.2.5　*Example* - In this simple example to illustrate the basic point, the stock held at the end of the year is carried forward at the cost of the unsold items. The result is that tax will only be assessed on the profit on the items which have actually been sold after setting their cost against the sale proceeds. The cost of the items carried forward is then set against the sales of those items when such sales subsequently take place.

Buy 10 items for £50	£500
Sell 6 items for £100	£600
Cash profit	£100
But there is a stock of unsold items	
To be added at cost (4 x £50)	£200
Actual profit in period	£300

2.2.6　While SSAP 9 also countenances the mark-to-market basis, stocktaking is classically done at the lower of cost or net realisable value. However, it may be noted that International Accounting Standards use a mark-to-market basis with fair value but this is not generally followed for farm stocktakings (save for publicly quoted companies for which IAS 41 should be followed).

2.2.7　Costs - Cost should be assessed by compiling the actual costs incurred. BIM 33135 interprets "cost" as:

"the total historical cost of bringing the relevant stock to its existing condition and location"

allowing that:

"where this is not precisely ascertainable, the aim should be to arrive at the closest approximation to historical cost that is practically attainable."

2.2.8　BIM33135 refers to rules introduced by the Companies Act 1981 (and then carried forward in the now replaced Companies Act 1985):

– purchase price is assessed as the price paid and any expenses incidental to its acquisition
– production cost is the sum of purchase price of the raw materials and consumables used and the "amount of the costs incurred by the company which are directly attributable to the production of that asset"
– the production cost *may* also include "A reasonable proportion of the costs incurred by the company which are only indirectly attributable to the production of that asset but only to the extent that they relate to the period of production ......"

For farming, these are pulled together by paragraph 3.1 of BEN 19.

2.2.9　In broad terms, overhead expenses fall to be included in this compilation of cost if they vary directly with volume of production – they are "directly attributable" to the production process. BIM33135 suggests more caution over overheads that accrue over time (perhaps such as rent except where, as may be the case for specialist crops, it has been expressly incurred just for that crop).

2.2.10　Farm stocktakings include not only input costs but also substantial in-house operational costs, from land preparation to harvesting, using farm labour and machinery. These may be based on CAAV Costings adjusted as appropriate – this is expressly recognised by BEN 19 at paragraph 3.1.5.1 – as these are calculated on cost basis, not on the basis that a contractor would use.

2.2.11   If relevant, it is assumed that inputs (perhaps fertiliser) bought first are used first – first in, first out.

2.2.12   It is not generally acceptable to use the replacement cost of inputs as at the balance sheet date, even if volatile markets mean that the market price is then very different from the actual cost, as has been seen with fertiliser values. In this case, the farmer has bought the fertiliser an input for use in making something else, not as trading stock itself.

2.2.13   While, in principle, each item of stock should be considered separately, paragraph 2 of SSAP9 allows similar items to be treated in groups or categories.

2.2.14   Deemed Costs - In recognition of common limitations on the availability of actual costs, a specific exception is allowed in certain circumstances for cattle, sheep and pigs and harvested crops when "deemed costs" may be used – applying prescribed percentages to the open market value of the animals or crops – but this basis is not available for any other species or any other items.

2.2.15   While "deemed costs" are essentially a proxy for costs, they are based on an assessment of market values on which guidance is given by valuations standards.

2.2.16   Net Realisable Value - In considering net realisable value, BIM33140 offers the interpretation:
> "… the **expected sale price** of the relevant stock in the condition in which it is expected to be sold in **the traders normal selling market**. From that value are **deducted the estimated further costs** which will have to be incurred to get the stock into its normal sale condition to arrive at the net realisable value."

2.2.17   SSAP9's paragraph 20 offers examples of where net realisable value is likely to be less than cost:
> – an increase in costs or a fall in selling prices
> – physical deterioration of stock
> – obsolescence of products
> – a decision as part of a company's marketing strategy to manufacture and sell products at a loss
> – errors in production or purchasing (note that this will cover mistakes resulting in excess stock or the purchasing of products which do not sell at all).

It also notes:
> "Furthermore, when stocks are held which are unlikely to be sold within the turnover period normal in that company (i.e. excess stocks), the impending delay in realisation increases the risk that the situations outlined in (a) to (c) above may occur before the stocks are sold and needs to be taken into account in assessing net realisable value."

2.2.18   BIM 33140 accepts that net realisable value "may be less than cost because of deterioration, obsolescence, or changes in demand".

2.2.19   The Choice Between Cost and Net Realisable Value – Net realisable value should only be used where it is less than cost.

2.2.20   SSAP 9 and FRS21 allow post-balance sheet date developments to be considered in deciding whether to use cost or net realisable value where there are "adjusting events": "events that provide additional evidence **relating to conditions**

existing at the balance sheet date and they require changes to be included in the financial statements". These are distinguished from "non-adjusting events" where conditions have changed since the balance sheet date. The following example highlights the difference between an adjusting event and a no-adjusting event in a farming situation:

> "**Example**: A farming company had one of its crops destroyed, after the balance sheet date but before the accounts were completed, by a disease which was present, albeit undetected, in that crop at the balance sheet date. In the financial statements being prepared it would be entitled to write that stock down to its nil net realisable value as that would be an adjusting event. On the other hand the destruction of a crop by fire, after the end of the accounting period but before the accounts were completed would be a non-adjusting event. It would not justify writing down that stock to a nil net realisable value in the financial statements being prepared."

In essence, the approach is that of the *Bwllfa* principle that facts which become clear after the date are preferable to contemporary speculation and accords with the HMRC guidance that the valuation follows a method that pays sufficient regard to the facts.

2.3 The Mark-to-Market Basis

2.3.1 Approach - Perhaps the key concept in International Accounting Standards is that valuations are to be fair rather than prudent. The accounting concept of "fair value" is defined as

> "the amount for which an asset could be exchanged or a liability settled, between knowledgeable, willing parties in an arm's length transaction."

Often a similar concept to market value, this is distinct from the concept of fair value in valuation standards which is more focussed on being air in the specific circumstances or between the specific parties.

2.3.2 While IAS 2 confirms that stocktakings are generally to be conducted on the conventional basis, IAS 41 sets out a fair value approach for agricultural stocktaking as regards growing and harvested crops and livestock. Consumables remain on the conventional basis. A version of this has been set out in Section 34 of the draft Financial Reporting Standard circulated for comments by the Accounting Standards Board in January 2012. This is discussed at Chapter 4.

2.3.3 The risk in this is of advancing unrealised (and potentially unrealisable) profits bringing them into tax earlier even though they may never be realised. The shift from a lower and more stable costs basis may also make farm accounts more volatile, especially with the greater volatility seen in many prices.

2.3.4 In agriculture, the structure is geared to appraising biological assets (living animals or plants the management of which constitutes agriculture) and valuing their income streams which may sit awkwardly with our underlying sense of land use. This may be more readily applicable to livestock and crops such as timber for which markets exist but creates issues for annual crops and crops grown for their produce for many of which there may be little or no market evidence.

2.3.5 This approach leads to a number of matters to be disclosed in accounts including a note of the biological assets themselves, reconciliation of changes in their stocktaking value, an explanation where fair value cannot be measured reliably, and the depreciation method and rates used.

2.3.6   As at the time of writing, HMRC's views on the status of IAS 41 were set out at BIM 31027:

> "... where there is a currently existing UK standard which applies to the transaction the UK standard should be followed rather than any international standard to bring the accounts and tax computation within the requirement of FA98/S42. "The current UK accounting standard which applies to stock valuations is SSAP9. This is supplemented for tax purposes by Business Economic Note BEN19, in which we describe stock valuation methods which are acceptable for tax purposes. We consider that self assessment returns, including the accounts and tax computations, which follow the principles in SSAP9 will comply with the requirements of FA98/S42.

> "IAS41 prescribes the accounting treatment related to agricultural activity. At present the Inland Revenue do not consider that its use is within generally accepted accounting practice as defined in ICTA88/S836A *[As ICTA has been repealed, strictly this is now Finance Act 2005, s.80]*. If accounts are prepared in accordance with IAS41 and tax computation adjustments are made to bring the stock valuation figures to SSAP9 figures this is acceptable for tax purposes."

2.4   Requirements for Limited Companies

2.4.1   **General** - While most farm businesses are either sole traders or partnerships, a minority of often larger farm businesses are structured as limited companies. These are subject to separate legal provisions which vary according to whether they are publicly quoted and a judgement of their size.

2.4.2   Accounts for limited companies are prepared, as required by EU law and s.393 of the Companies Act 2006, to show a true and fair view of the company's state of affairs on which the auditor or other accountant expresses his opinion.

2.4.3   The Companies Act 2006 requires greater disclosure of information in the accounts of limited companies than for sole traders or partnerships (though limited liability partnerships are required to disclose accounts). The accounts have to be filed for public inspection at Companies House.

2.4.4   Many limited companies have to be audited. It is a statutory obligation where the company:
- has an annual turnover exceeding £6.5 million or gross assets over £3.26 million
- is part of a group that exceeds those limits;
- is a PLC or a banking, insurance or finance company (or a subsidiary of one of these).

2.4.5   Valuers should assume that a stocktaking for a limited company will be used to supply figures that are included in publicly available accounts.

2.4.6   The valuer has thus a considerable duty of care when undertaking a stocktaking for a limited company. Valuers should be particularly careful about obtaining and retaining evidence to support the figures they include in the stocktaking. It is even more important to work closely with the client's accountant than for sole traders or partnerships.

2.4.7   The Fourth Schedule to the Companies Act 1985 expressly required stock to be included in financial statements at cost (purchase price or production cost) or (and only if this would be lower) at net realisable value (paragraphs 22 and 23 of the Schedule) While repealed by the Companies Act 2006, these provisions anyway stand under general analysis (save where International Accounting Standards or International Financial Reporting Standards apply) and may be re-enacted in regulations under the new Act.

2.4.8   The Schedule's Paragraph 27(3) also required a company to state in a note to the accounts the difference between the replacement costs of the stocks and their book amount where this difference is material.

2.4.9   **Application of the Costs Basis** - The accountancy bodies have set out their requirements in Statement of Standard Accounting Practice number 9 (SSAP 9). The basis used in the accounts for accounting for stock must be disclosed. Costs should comprise the expenditure which has been incurred in the normal course of business in bringing the stock into its present location and condition.

2.4.10   The expenses incidental to purchase of stocks should be included in the purchase price.

2.4.11   Directly attributable production costs must be included (see 3.1 of BEN 19).

2.4.12   In compiling actual costs incurred by a limited company, the labour of company directors must be taken into account (in contrast to the position of sole traders or partnerships). The labour figure used, however, should not necessarily be pro rata to the directors' earnings; the value of their time spent tractor driving may not equate to time spent on higher value activities.

2.4.13   If no detailed records are available to compute actual costs, then the deemed cost basis is acceptable where it is allowed (see section 3.7 below) but this must not reduce any item below its purchase cost.

2.4.14   Overheads that are only indirectly related to the production of the stock in question should only be included if the accountant directs – this is only usually required for larger commercial companies. If interest charges are included as an indirect cost, that fact must be stated together with the amount.

2.4.15   **Mark-to-Market Basis** - EU Regulation 1606/2002 (amended by 1725/2003) requires listed companies to draw up consolidated accounts in accordance with IFRS. Other EU regulations make more specific provisions. In addition, the Government has allowed that other companies and limited liability partnerships are able to use IFRS. These have a general emphasis on fair value (as defined by the accounting standards rather than valuation standards) as the basis for accounting judgements. In this context fair value is akin to market value.

2.4.16   Within IFRS, International Accounting Standard 41 (IAS41) relating to agricultural stocktaking introduces a fair value basis rather than a prudent basis for growing and harvested crops and livestock while consumables and other stocktakings for production businesses remain on a costs basis. A version of this is under discussion for application to the largest farm businesses in the United Kingdom and Ireland. This is disused in Chapter 4.

2.4.17 The awkwardness of the fair value approach for farming businesses has meant that few have adopted IFRS voluntarily while the UK's Financial Reporting Standards for Smaller Entities (FRSSE) has, so far, disapplied it from all but the very largest businesses that agricultural valuers may meet.

2.4.18 **Auditors' Inquiries** - Auditors, like valuers, are expected to exercise reasonable care so will not necessarily accept a stocktaking valuation without question. Since 23rd December 1995 they have been guided by the Statement of Auditing Standards SAS 520, using the work of an expert (SAS 520, see Annexe K to these guidance notes) which provides guidance on obtaining audit evidence from someone with special skill, knowledge and experience in a particular field other than auditing. The auditor is asked to assess, among other matters, whether the sources of information, assumptions and methods used by the expert are appropriate, sufficient, relevant and reliable. The auditor may wish to verify the basis of the stocktaking and confirm the procedures used to ensure that purchases and sales around the year end have been correctly included in the stocks or excluded from them as appropriate. In some circumstances the auditor may wish to attend the stocktaking inspection. Valuers will need to demonstrate to auditors that there is adequate supporting evidence for the stocktaking figures.

3. COMMENTARY ON "BEN 19"

Note – The text of what was BEN 19 is set out, section by section, in shaded boxes with each section followed by a commentary.

3.1 Introduction

3.1.1 Business Economic Note 19, Farming Stock Valuations for Income Tax Purposes was published in 1993 following discussions with industry and professional bodies, including the CAAV.

3.1.2 While Business Economic Notes have since been withdrawn as a series, the text is preserved with its paragraph numbers at HMRC's Business Income Manual 55410. It has also been published as Help Sheet HS 232.

3.1.3 This chapter takes BIM 55410 by sections and offers a commentary on points that have arisen.

3.1.4 The Inland Revenue published a gloss on a number of aspects of BEN 19 with an article in the May 1993 Tax Bulletin coinciding with its publication – see Annexe D

Structure of "BEN 19"

3.1.5 After an introduction and a statement of general principles, the core of the paper covers livestock, growing and harvested crops. More specific sections then follow on price with co-operatives, the treatment of grants and subsidies and consumables. A final section considers the use of deemed costs.

---

1. INTRODUCTION

1.1 This statement explains the basis of valuation of farm stock at the end of periods of account which is acceptable to Inspectors of Taxes. It has been prepared to assist farmers and their professional advisers. It has been prepared after consultation between the Inland Revenue, the Central Association of Agricultural Valuers, the Institute of Chartered Accountants in England and Wales, the Institute of Taxation, the Royal Institution of Chartered Surveyors, the Country Landowners Association and the NFU. It supersedes all previous arrangements made by the Inland Revenue and the NFU. It does not affect rights of appeal in individual cases.

1.2 Other methods of valuation may also be acceptable to Inspectors of Taxes in particular cases provided they are recognised by the accountancy profession as a whole as giving a true and fair view of the results for the period concerned and do not violate the taxing statutes as interpreted by the Courts.

1.3 A valuation which, although in form made on a recognised basis, pays insufficient attention to the facts will not be acceptable.

3.2   General Principles
3.2.1   This statement of basic principles affirms:
  – the use of the accruals basis and so the need for stocktaking (paragraph 2.1)
  – that it is to be done on lower of cost of production or net realisable value (paragraphs 2.2 and 2.3)
  – the desirability of consistency of approach between years (paragraph 2.4)
  – that the taxpayer should advise HMRC if changing an accounting policy (paragraph 2.4).

3.2.2   In a specific comment, paragraph 2.8 allows that livestock may be valued in batches of animals similar as to type or quality rather than singly.

---

2.   GENERAL PRINCIPLES

2.1   The reason for valuing stock at the end of an accounting period is to identify and carry forward those costs which were incurred before that date but will not give rise to income until a later period. By carrying forward those costs they can be matched with the income when it arises. Profit will be understated if stock is not brought in.

2.2   However, if there is no reasonable expectation that the proceeds from the sale of the stock in a future period will be enough to cover the costs, then relief for the expected loss may be obtained in the period for which the accounts are being prepared by valuing the stock at what it is expected to realise when sold in the normal course of trade.

2.3   For tax purposes we are looking for a figure (commonly referred to as a valuation) which represents the cost, or, if lower, the net realisable value of the stock.

2.4   In some circumstances there may be more than one acceptable method of computing the value of stock but the basis of valuation in a particular case should be consistent. If it is decided to change the basis of valuation the Inspector of Taxes should be advised when the accounts are submitted. The Revenue's practice on changes of basis in valuation is set out in Statement of Practice 3/90. *[SP 3/90 is now obsolete.]*

2.5   Occasionally Inspectors discover that the stock figure in the accounts is net of a provision (reserve), e.g. for dilapidations. If the creation of such a provision is considered appropriate the Inspector should be made fully aware of it. Provisions are only allowable for tax purposes if profits would not be properly stated in their absence and the amount referable to the year can be quantified with reasonable accuracy. Even if these conditions are met tax law provides that some provisions are not allowable for tax purposes (e.g. for repairs to premises which are not allowable unless expended).

2.6.   The value of stock is primarily a matter of fact which is ultimately to be decided by the Commissioners in the absence of agreement.

2.7   Valuation problems can be complex, and farmers normally seek the assistance of accountants and agricultural valuers and surveyors. But this is not compulsory and some farmers prepare their own valuations.

2.8   Although strictly livestock should be valued on an animal by animal basis, it is acceptable for farmers to value animals of a similar type and quality together on a global or average basis classified according to age. If deemed cost is used (see paragraph 7 below) home bred animals should be distinguished from animals which have been brought in.

2.9.   If tax is lost or delayed as a result of incorrect valuation of stock then interest and penalties may be due in addition to the tax.

3.3   Livestock, Growing and Harvested Crops

3.3.1   This section forms the main body of BEN 19, focussing on production costs defining the direct costs for, first, livestock and, then, growing and harvested crops that are to be considered as distinguished from indirect costs that are excluded. It states when deemed costs are acceptable – more detail on this is at 3.7 below. Finally, it considers the assessment of net realisable value where this is the appropriate method.

3.   LIVESTOCK, GROWING AND HARVESTED CROPS
3.1   Production Cost
Production cost is the actual cost of getting the stock into its condition and location at the balance sheet date. Farm stock valuations should include the costs directly attributable to producing or rearing the stock in question. From an accountancy point of view it is preferable but not mandatory, except in the case of certain limited companies, also to include a reasonable proportion of the costs which are only indirectly attributable to the production of the stock to the extent that those costs relate to the period of production as this will result in a more accurate matching of costs with related sales income. Either method, if applied consistently, is acceptable to Inspectors of Taxes.

3.1.1   Direct Costs
3.1.1.1 Costs which are directly attributable to buying, producing and growing the livestock or crops should be included. Such costs will consist not only of the expenses of acquiring the "raw materials" e.g. seeds but also of any expenses which directly relate to producing or rearing the stock in question. There can be no definitive list, but the following are examples of direct costs:

3.1.2   Livestock
- Purchase costs or
- Insemination costs plus additional maternal feed costs in excess of maintenance,
PLUS costs of rearing to the valuation date or maturity if earlier including:
- Feed costs including forage,
- Vets' fees including drugs,
- Drenches and other medicines,
- Ringing, cutting and dehorning,
- Supervisory employee or contract labour costs.

3.1.3   Growing and Harvested Crops
- Seeds,
- Fertilisers,
- Beneficial Sprays (The term beneficial sprays includes preventative sprays and means any sprays which are not applied to remedy a particular infestation or crop deficiency),

16

- Seasonal licence payments (e.g. short term hire of land to grow a particular crop) but not normal farm rents,
- Drying,
- Storage,
- Employee (including director) or contract labour and direct machinery costs (e.g. fuel, servicing, rental, spares and the reduction in value due to wear and tear caused by actual usage for the activity concerned) incurred on,
- Cultivations,
- Crop working,
- Harvesting.

3.1.4 Indirect costs
3.1.4.1 Once again there can be no definitive list of indirect items, but examples of such costs are:
- depreciation and maintenance of farm buildings
- rent and rates (excluding licence payments added under 3.2.2 above) *(sic this should be 3.1.3.)*
- general employee (including director) or contract labour and machinery costs.

3.1.5 Cost to be based on expenditure incurred
3.1.5.1 Except where the deemed cost method is used (see 3.2) cost must represent the actual costs incurred by the particular farmer on producing the stock as established from his own records. Larger and specialised businesses, such as intensive pig rearing units, will usually have adequate records to compute cost. The current Guide to Costings as issued by the Central Association of Agricultural Valuers and figures produced by other independent institutions provide useful models to help farmers establish their own costs.

3.1.5.2 Labour costs should not include anything for the notional cost of own labour for sole proprietors or partners.

3.2. Deemed cost acceptable in some circumstances
3.2.1. If it is not possible to ascertain actual costs from the farmer's records, Inspectors will accept deemed cost valuations (see paragraph 7 below).

3.3. Net Realisable Value
3.3.1 If there is no reasonable expectation that the net realisable value of stock will cover costs incurred then the stock should be stated at net realisable value.

3.3.2. Net realisable value consists of:
- The sale proceeds that it is anticipated will be received from the eventual disposal of the stock in the condition in which the farmer intended at his balance sheet date subsequently to market it. It is important to note that the valuation should be made on a normal commercial basis, for instance, it is not acceptable to value stock on the basis that it would have been sold in a forced sale on the balance sheet date in its then possibly immature state.

PLUS
- Grants and subsidies intended to augment the sale prices of stocks (see *5.2*).
- For breeding/production animals the ancillary stream of income from the sale of their progeny and produce.

LESS
- The further costs to be incurred in getting the stock into marketable condition and then marketing, selling and distributing that stock. Where the proceeds from the sale of progeny/produce are brought in then the costs relating to their production and marketing should also be deducted.

3.3.3 It is not acceptable to treat cull value as the only future revenue from production animals as this does not recognise the value of the future income stream from the produce and/or progeny.

3.3.4 The Revenue recognises, however, that farmers may not have the extensive records necessary to calculate net realisable value with reasonable accuracy, therefore:
- For production animals such as laying hens and breeding sows which are not usually sold except for slaughter at the end of their productive lives, the Revenue will accept that a reasonable approximation of the net realisable value is the value at the balance sheet date arrived at by consistently writing off the cost, down to anticipated cull value, on a straight line or other appropriate basis over the animal's expected productive life.
- For other production animals the Revenue will accept the use of the open market value of animals of the same kind, quality and condition based on the assumption that there is a willing buyer and a willing seller of the particular animal as a production animal at the balance sheet date.

3.3.5 Where net realisable value is used as being less than cost the Inspector may want to establish the basis of valuation.

General

3.3.2   BEN 19 expects the actual costs of production to be used unless it is not possible to ascertain them with reasonable accuracy from the farmer's records. The basic requirement is for information on:
- physical inputs
- cultivations undertaken.

The demands of self assessment combine with the needs of business management to encourage farmers to maintain good records capable of providing a crop valuation up to and beyond harvest.

3.3.3   As other traditional bases of valuations, including a waygoing tenant right style valuation as approved when stocktakings were first required for tax in 1942, are no longer approved, silage should be valued just as any other harvested crop - consuming value is not a normal accounting policy.

3.3.4   Where a farmer has used market value (as is sometimes found for crops in store at the balance sheet date) then it would be consistent to retain that basis. Any change to a cost basis would need to be agreed between the client, the valuer and the accountant and then declared in the valuation and in the accounts.

3.3.5   **Direct Costs (paragraphs 3.1.1 to 3.1.3)** - In calculating actual costs of production, the valuer should include the "direct" costs of the operation which contribute to the crop. For crops, these will include costs connected with field operations to grow crops by way of seeds, fertilisers and sprays which, together with the necessary machinery costs, must be counted as a cost to production.

3.3.6 Sprays – beneficial or remedial? (paragraph 3.1.3) – BEN 19 draws a distinction between sprays that enhance the crops and sprays that preserve it.

3.3.7 Sprays that are applied as part of normal husbandry to improve the crop or as a general preventative measure are regarded as *beneficial* by nature and so, as enhancement expenditure, their costs should be included in the costs carried forward in stock.

3.3.8 By contrast, *remedial sprays* are those applied to correct, eradicate, or limit an identified disease or infestation. They preserve rather than enhance the value, and as such are not carried forward as a cost in stocktaking valuations.

3.3.9 Indirect Costs (paragraph 3.1.4) - The valuer should exclude the "indirect" costs – those costs which are incurred whether or not an operation is undertaken. Thus, rent, as with other fixed overheads, should be excluded unless (as may be the case for short term land) it is directly associated with the specific crop that is being assessed as a stock. Thus, rent on land taken for a season for potatoes must be counted as a cost to their production (except for a limited company).

3.3.10 Labour (paragraphs 3.1.3, 3.1.4 and 3.1.5.2) - BEN 19 expects actual costs of production to exclude the time of the self-employed owner ("proprietorial labour") which is not a cost (see its paragraph 3.1.5.2).

3.3.11 This means that the labour of the farmer where he is a sole trader or a partner should not be taken into account because it is not a cost. Direct labour by company directors and employees (including family members) should be brought into account because it is a cost – they are employees. The charge need not be at a rate which is pro rata to that for other hours spent by that person during the year on more important items. Thus, a company director working as a tractor driver would have a cost figure which is less than a company director who is carrying out boardroom duties.

3.3.12 CAAV Costings (paragraph 3.1.5.1) – Costs are to be those actually incurred by the farmer in producing livestock or crops. That must include the costs of cultivations and other operations using the farmer's own machinery. While the farmer will have bills for work by contractors the costs of his own operations must be constructed.

3.3.13 The CAAV's Costings of Agricultural Operations are expressly recognised by BEN 19 (and so also Self Assessment Help Sheet HS 232 and HMRC's Business Income Manual which reproduce it) as a basis for establishing actual costs of production. The CAAV publishes its Schedule of Costings each autumn for a wide range of agricultural operations with effect for the year following. The proprietorial labour of a sole trader or partner will need to be excluded and the Costings show the figures with and without this element, using the rate for agricultural labour. The Costings must be further adjusted as necessary to reflect the circumstances of the farm. CAAV members can obtain the detailed working papers that underpin the published Schedule to aid that task of adjustment.

3.3.14 Depreciation in Costings (paragraph 3.1.4) – The wearing out of fixed assets is considered in different ways for accounts and tax computations. It is assessed as depreciation for accounts. However, tax computations disregard depreciation, making capital allowances available instead. Thus, tax accounts are produced by adding depreciation back before deducting capital allowances to arrive at taxable income.

3.3.15   Lord Hoffman explained the position in opening the House of Lords decision in the *William Grant (Distillers) Limited* and *Mars* cases on this issue:

"The method of computing trading profits for the purposes of income and corporation tax has been settled for many years. First you compute the profits on a basis which gives a true and fair view of the taxpayer's profits or losses in the relevant period. Then you make any adjustments expressly required for tax purposes, such as adding back deductions which the taxing statute forbids. The classic formulation of this method is by Sir John Pennycuick V-C in *Odeon Associated Theatres Ltd v Jones* (1970) 48 TC 257, 272-273 and it has now been codified in section 42(1) of the Finance Act 1998:

"For the purposes of Case I or II of Schedule D the profits of a trade profession or vocation must be computed on an accounting basis which gives a true and fair view, subject to any adjustment required or authorised by law in computing profits for those purposes.'""

3.3.16   Both firms had divided the depreciation of fixed assets that arose in the year so that they could allocate appropriate fractions to:

– the production of goods that were sold in the year deducted directly from the year's sales
– the production of goods that were unsold by the balance sheet date (presumably a significant issue for aged malt whiskies) with that element of depreciation carried forward within stocks for the accounts.

The House of Lords found that the resulting statement of accounts was in accordance with accounting standards and gave a true and fair view. The result was that the depreciation included in stocks was no longer to be added back when converting the accounts to the tax computation. That element of depreciation is then added back when the resulting stock is subsequently sold when it is relevant to the true profit for the year of disposal.

3.3.17   Following the March 2007 House of Lords' decision in the *Grant* and *Mars* cases, HMRC accepted that it is anomalous for the stocktaking to include any element of depreciation that is also covered by capital allowances. While this is to the taxpayer's initial advantage, that advantage is unwound when stock is ultimately sold and so more swiftly in most farming cases than for a malt whisky distiller.

3.3.18   This is an issue for all types of business, not just agricultural ones. HMRC has advised by letter that:

"The adjustment is mandatory for all businesses whatever their size. An add back for depreciation has always been required for depreciation that is carried in stock – it is only the timing of the adjustment that has been changed by the House of Lords decision."

3.3.19   The significance of this is that not only do the CAAV's annual Costings of Agricultural Operations include machinery depreciation but the value of the machinery used results in this forming a significant element of the cost of most operations which is now separately identified in the CAAV's Costings to assist valuers in reporting on the stocktaking.

3.3.20   The key practical point is that this is an issue for the tax computation, rather than the accounts themselves. Thus the valuer should seek clear instructions which are likely to ask for:

– the stocktaking figure including machinery depreciation to provide the figure for the accounts

– the element within that figure representing machinery depreciation to assist the accountant in the tax computation. The accountant may wish to be able to identify the depreciation element for growing crops, crops in store and unproductive work for the purposes of this adjustment.

3.3.21   The sample Report at Annexe B allows for this to be reported.

3.3.22   HMRC has advised that it considers that deemed costs (see section 3.7 below) will also include depreciation and so also require adjustment in moving from the accounts to the tax computation. This may perhaps usually be best addressed by assessing a typical percentage that would be represented by depreciation as compared to all the other components of cost. It might thus be that a different percentage would be used for livestock than for harvested crops.

3.3.23   Where, as can be the case for farmers with old or second-hand machinery, the accountant finds that the depreciation in the accounts is markedly less than the depreciation reported using standard costings figures he may according to the circumstances and his approach either:
- accept that this is anyway simply an arithmetical adjustment in a situation where the accountant's records may be distorted by the trade-in terms for machinery or profits on disposals, or
- judge the reasonableness of the situation and if there is a substantial discrepancy return to the valuer for further discussion.

3.3.24   Actual or Deemed Costs - It is usually possible to arrive at actual costs readily on most arable enterprises, particularly with the help of CAAV Costings. However, it can often prove more difficult to identify actual costs on many livestock farms where the attribution of forage costs to individual animals (or classes of animal) may not be well recorded – equally, some livestock farmers keep excellent records. The use of deemed costs (see section 7 of BEN 19 and the commentary in section 3.7 below) will be more often found on livestock enterprises.

3.3.25   It is acceptable for a stocktaking to use actual costs for some categories and deemed costs for others. As examples;
- a stocktaking might use actual costs for crops but deemed costs for cattle.
- one group of cattle can be on the actual cost method and the remainder on the deemed cost method (crops may be similarly divided).
- a consistent approach over time is important and advisable. For crops, this means consistency over a reasonable period of time; for livestock, consistency over the time an animal or group of animals is held by the business.

3.3.26   Both actual and deemed costs are valid under BEN 19: the use of deemed costs is an approved practice and the use of actual costs is a legal entitlement *(Gallagher v Jones)*. Switching between actual costs and deemed costs is not recommended without proper commercial justification. The method chosen should be consistently applied unless there is sufficient reason to make a change. It is possible to switch from deemed costs to the actual cost method of valuation and, where this is done, it would be good practice to state this in the valuation (and then in the accounts).

3.3.27   Net realisable value (paragraphs 3.3.1 to 3.3.5) – This is only to be used when it is reasonably expected to be lower than the actual costs of production (paragraphs 2.2 and 3.3 of BEN 19).

3.3.28   Net realisable value will usually be market value less the costs of putting the item in question into condition for sale and then the costs of sale.

3.3.29   Occasionally there may be a reason for distinguishing between net realisable value and market value (e.g. where compensation is paid for notifiable diseases). It may be that a simple market value basis would produce an unrealistically low forced sale basis.

3.3.30   The net realisable value of breeding stock should not be confined to the simple cull value but should reflect its production potential.

3.3.31   It is unlikely that valuations will result in negative values though these might arise from the costs of disposal. Should such a situation arise, it is suggested that the positive value is entered with a note regarding costs of disposal for the accountant to consider.

Procedure for Arable Crops
3.3.32   The valuer should establish an appropriate reconciliation of the crops ascertaining the acres grown, harvest weights, and sales away from the farm prior to the balance sheet date as well as the crops in store.

3.3.33   HMRC encourages valuations on the basis of actual costs of production. These should be calculated using the basis set out in BEN 19 at section 3.1.3.

3.3.34   Unsold severed crops (but not growing crops) can be assessed on the basis of deemed cost (at 75 per cent of their market value) but HMRC encourages the use of actual costs.

3.3.35   Tillages, Cultivations, Fertilisers Applied, - All costs attributable to the growing of a crop which is unsold or unused at the balance sheet date.

3.3.36   Annual fertiliser applications made as part of normal husbandry may be written off within the year, thus making the concept of UMVs and RMVs redundant for accounting. In appraising other applications (such as lime), the valuer may have regard to the intention with which they are applied but should be consistent in his approach.

3.3.37   UMVs, RMVs and Dilapidations – When Income Tax was first generally applied to farmers' accounts (rather than the value of their land) in 1942, stocktaking was to be constructed on the basis of a tenant right valuation (a waygoing basis). This has now been acceptable since 1957 as made clear by the Inland Revenue in the May 1993 Tax Bulletin note covering the publication of BEN 19. Equally, dilapidations are not to be deducted for stocktaking purposes.

3.3.38   Where items that are now redundant for stocktaking, such as UMVs, RMVs and dilapidations, were previously included in the stocktaking, BIM55455 considers unexhausted manurial values of fertilisers applied to the land and also the equivalent sod value of grass and advises that:
        – there is no requirement to include them in stocktaking
        – whether included or not, the policy should be followed consistently.

3.3.39   In new cases, they should be noted and reported to the accountant who will carry them forward in perpetuity as a balance sheet item without subsequent adjustment until the business ceases when any difference between initial and final figures is then taken to the profit and loss account.

3.3.40   Arable By-products - Straw and other outputs such as sugar beet tops, pea haulm and small potatoes which are relevant by-products of an arable crop can be included on a cost of production basis. Where the main crop is also dealt with on this basis, the costs of production of the by-product would normally be no more than baling and carting.

3.3.41   Alternatively, it is possible to treat by-products on a deemed cost basis at 75% of market value once they are a harvested crop.

3.3.42   Failed Crops - Where a crop has substantially failed, it may be necessary to use a net realisable value basis. If an insurance claim has been lodged and a payment is anticipated, it should be reflected in the valuation or reported to the accountant. The status and extent of any claims should be established.

3.3.43   Perennial Crops and Grass Leys - Perennial crops, such as asparagus, soft and top fruit, hops, miscanthus and vines, where more than one crop will be expected from the plants are not mentioned in BEN 19. HMRC has set out its approach to short rotation coppice in BIM 55120 (which has superseded the statement in the October 1995 Tax Bulletin) – see Annexe E. That takes the approach that the initial establishment costs should be regarded as capital as the plants become part of the land (and so the costs involved in any final removal would be a capital expense). The subsequent direct costs of managing the plants and harvesting the crop are seen as a matter for the stocktaking where they need to be matched against the prospect of subsequent receipts. It is suggested that costs of replacing plants be treated in the same way. BIM 55120 also prefers indirect costs (such as rent, building maintenance and general management costs) to be handled in this way but accepts that in most cases they will be seen as costs for the general farm accounts rather than attributable to stocks (see 3.3.9 above).

3.3.44   Alternatively, the economics of the operation may be reflected most practically by writing down the cost of the establishment over the expected life of the crop.

3.3.45   For grass leys, it is suggested that establishment costs should be the basis in the first year, if no crop is taken. The figures for subsequent years should be based on the establishment costs written down over the life of the ley together with any costs incurred in each year on a 'no crop off' basis. There are other approaches to the treatment of subsequent years – some accountants prefer leys to be treated as a perennial crop.

Livestock
3.3.46   The same underlying principle that stocktaking should be at cost, or if lower, net realisable value applies to livestock.

3.3.47   The heads for actual costs for consideration are set out in paragraph 3.1.2 of BEN 19.

3.3.48   The information for actual costs may be more readily available for pedigree and dairy herds than for more general livestock enterprises.

3.3.49   If it is not possible to ascertain actual costs from the farmer's records, Inspectors of Taxes will accept deemed cost valuation for cattle (at 60 per cent of market value) and for sheep and pigs (both at 75 per cent).

3.3.50   Even where a farmer elects to use deemed costs these cannot be used in all circumstances. Where deemed costs cannot be used (as for stock other than cattle, sheep or pigs, or stock brought in), actual costs should be used.

3.3.51   Other stock such as deer, ostriches and alpaca cannot be valued on deemed costs

3.3.52   Current net realisable value should, however, be used if at any balance sheet date it would be lower than cost.

3.3.53   Breeding Stock not on the Herd Basis - The cull value of production animal is not an acceptable basis for stocktaking for tax purposes (see BEN 19 paragraphs 3.3. and 7.1.3, the May 1993 Tax Bulletin (see Annexe D) and BIM 55415). It is rare for a breeding animal to be purchased with a view to immediate culling. The animals are to be included at the lower of cost and net realisable value.

3.3.54   Where using net realisable value, this must reflect the flow of income that is expected from the animal's progeny. Where production animals such as sows and poultry are retained and not sold save for slaughter, HMRC will accept writing-off the cost to cull value on a straight line or other appropriate basis over the expected life of the animal (see the framework suggested at paragraph 3.3.4 of BEN 19).

3.3.55   Working Horses – BIM55440 allows these to be treated as either stock in trade or a fixed capital asset (in which case a home bred horse can have its value estimated at 85 per cent of its current market value). Once the choice of basis has been made, it should be adhered to consistently.

3.3.56   Major Livestock Disease Outbreaks – Disease control measures can mean that, for a period, there are no markets for livestock. That does not mean they have no value. Relevant issues were reviewed in the Inland Revenue Press Release of 29th April 1996 on BSE and Farm Stocktaking Valuations (see Annexe I). Parts of this guidance may be relevant for future outbreaks.

3.3.57   Checklist
In preparing the stocktaking, the valuer is likely to require information as to both livestock and crops.

Livestock
> Identify livestock by appropriate categories (breed, age, weight, state of pregnancy, etc
> Establishing closing numbers by category
> If the stocktaking is conducted other than at the year end date, consider reviewing the animal movement records to ensure an accurate assessment
> Costs incurred in production (where obtainable)
> Notes (e.g. information derived from farmer, difficulty in establishing exact numbers of hill sheep)

Crops
Growing crops
> Area of each crop
> Cultivations undertaken since the last harvest
> Seeds, fertilisers and sprays

Severed crops
> Areas from which each crop has taken
> Yields of each crop
> Sales and movements of each crop before the accounting period
> Volumes of each crop in store (on and off the farm) with weights if known
> For actual costs – the cultivations for each crop and seeds, sprays and fertilisers

General

Does the farmer sell through a co-operative? (see section 4 of BEN 19)

3.4 Co-operatives

> **4.   CO-OPERATIVES**
>
> 4.1   In the same way as any other stock held by a farmer, stock marketed through co-operatives acting as agent for the farmer must be included in the valuation unless it has been sold.
>
> 4.2   Stock held off the farm which is identifiable as belonging to the farmer must also be included.
>
> 4.3   Where stock held off the farm has been pooled and cannot be identified as belonging to a particular farmer the unsold proportion must be included. This may be computed by taking A x B/C where A is the amount in the pool which came from the farmer, B is the amount in the pool not sold at the valuation date and C is the amount in the pool not sold at the valuation date plus the amount sold from it up to that date.
>
> 4.4   Where a co-operative acts as agent for the farmer but the relevant stock can be identified as not being part of a pool, no apportionment is necessary. It should be included in the valuation (see 4.2 above).
>
> 4.5   Stock which has been sold to a co-operative which does not act as agent should not be included in the valuation.

Sales through co-operatives

3.4.1   Where any sales are made through a co-operative, the valuer may need to ask:
- if the co-operative acts as agent for the farmer or as principal in its sales
- if there is a statement of sales prior to the accounting date?
- where is the stock stored (by category)?

3.4.2   Harvested crops held by co-operatives should be treated in the same way as any other stock held by a farmer. It is necessary to look at the contract between the farmer and the co-operative to ascertain the point of sale. Usually, the co-operative acts as agent with all grain accounted for in a pool. Where the co-operative acts as principal rather than as agent, grain is deemed to be sold when it leaves the farm.

3.4.3   If grain is pooled and away from the farm, ascertain the percentage of the pool that is unsold at the year end and apply this to the tonnage of the farmer's grain using the formula $a \times b \div c$ where
- a is the total amount of farmer's grain stored in the pool
- b is the tonnage of pool unsold, and
- c the total tonnage of the pool.

Where pooled grain remains on the farm, the farmer's grain is still physically identifiable and should be valued.

3.4.4   Advanced payments should not be treated as sales except insofar as there has been physical movement of the farmer's grain off the farm and the co-operative is acting as principal or where grain has been sold from the pool where the co-operative is agent.

3.4.5   *Example* – A co-operative where the crop is owned by a farmer but stored in a pool in the central store (not on the farm) and the co-operative acts as the farmer's agent

Farmer consigns crop to co-operative	500 tonnes
Stored in 5,000 tonne pool	
The co-operative has sold	2,000 tonnes
So the farmer has made a deemed sale of	200 tonnes
Leaving in store for his stocktaking	300 tonnes

3.5   Grants and Subsidies

3.5.1   BEN 19 was drafted to apply the analysis of accounting policies to the subsidy system of livestock premia and arable area aid with associated set-aside established by the MacSharry reforms of the CAP in 1992. This guidance was subsequently developed by statements in the Tax Bulletin.

3.5.2   The analysis below shows that arable area aid, as an aid to sales, was to be included in the stocktaking to the extent that the crop had not been sold at the balance sheet date. Guidance was also given on the treatment of livestock payments.

3.5.3   The Single Payment Scheme was introduced in 2005 as a subsidy system decoupled from production and so not relevant to stocktaking. It has now replaced the previous subsidy schemes.

3.5.4   A new coupled scheme, the Scottish Beef Calf Scheme was introduced under devolved powers in 2005.

---

5.   GRANTS AND SUBSIDIES – EFFECT ON STOCK VALUATIONS

5.1   Grants and subsidies towards specific expenses should be regarded as reducing those expenses. If those expenses are included in the cost for stock valuation then the figure used should be the net cost after deducting the related grants.

5.2   Grants and subsidies intended to augment the sale prices of stocks should be taken into account in calculating their net realisable values.

3.5.5   When taking on a new client, it might be prudent to ask for a copy of the SPS form as part of collecting relevant evidence, particularly to ensure that the valuer knows of all the fields on which production may have happened. This would be one check on the probative quality of other evidence offered by the client and assist the reconciliation of reported gross sales and grain in store with the declared area used to produce it.

3.5.6   HMRC generally expects accounts to be prepared on the accruals basis. The consequences can vary according to the different types of payments and the reasons for and timing of subsidies. It will be necessary for the valuer to understand clearly what accounting policies are being used in the client's accounts.

3.5.7   Recognition on receipt brings subsidies supporting general trading income into account as they are received.

3.5.8   Recognition on entitlement brings subsidies into account at the time when the farmer has qualified for the payment by fulfilling the material obligations required under the particular scheme and so is entitled to receive it although he may not be paid for some time. It is this rule that has required careful analysis under the single payment regime.

3.5.9   Recognition on sale brings subsidies into account where they are held to be a support to sales income when the item to which they relate is sold, irrespective of the date of receipt or entitlement. Under this basis, the old Arable Area Payment Scheme payments and Protein Premium payments are recognised as income in a particular accounting period only to the extent to which that crop has been sold prior to the balance sheet date.

3.5.10   Grants that are intended to reduce costs should be treated as such and so will reduce the cost of stocks as appropriate.

3.5.11   Single Payment - Analysis by the ICAEW and ICAS in conjunction with the CAAV and HMRC identified that the Single Payment is recognised in the accounts on the taxpayer becoming entitled to it. From 2005 to 2007, this was held to be on the termination of the ten month period (or if two were claimed, the latter one) declared on the claim form (SP5 in England; SAF in Wales and Scotland). When the ten month period requirement was dropped for 2008, analysis of the qualifications for entitlement resulted in advice that it was for professional discretion to choose whether it should be the May 15th date of claim or the December 31st end of the year for paramount agricultural use.

3.5.12   Whichever the date, the Single Payment is not a matter for the stocktaking. The Inland Revenue issued its initial views on the Single Payment Scheme in its special edition of the Tax Bulletin of June 2005 which has now been followed by the pages in HMRC's Business Income Manual starting at BIM 55125.

3.5.13   Arable area payments and equivalent schemes were regarded as aids to sales and so only taken into account to the extent to which the crop has been sold in the relevant accounting period. At Annexe G, the HMRC Tax Bulletin of February 1994 outlined the approaches taken and is retained in this edition of this paper lest future schemes require reference to it. These schemes are now no longer relevant save in so far as there may be a need to take account of final claims under the Protein Crop Premium and the Area Payment for Nuts.

3.5.14   Livestock payments have traditionally been recognised on their receipt. Their treatment was covered by the article in the Tax Bulletin of December 1994, Animal Grants, included here at Annexe H and retained in this edition of this paper lest future schemes require reference to it. The position is now considered by BIM 55430. Again, these schemes are now no longer relevant but the guidance would also apply to the Scottish Beef Calf Scheme (see 3.5.16).

3.5.15   In addition to the policies of SSAPs 2 and 9, the valuer should thus seek instructions as to the basis on which to account for any payments other than the Single Payment. These remain covered by previous Revenue guidance given in the Tax Bulletin of December 1994 (see Annexe H).

3.5.16   Scottish Beef Calf Scheme – As with the pre-2005 livestock subsidy schemes, BIM55430 advises that, being payable in respect of individual identified live animals, this may need to be taken into account when using deemed costs:
　　　　– where the receipt has been recorded as income in the year, there is no effect
　　　　– where it has not been so recorded but
　　　　　○ the subsidy has been applied for and
　　　　　○ has a material effect on the value of the animal
　　　　then it operates to increase the animal's market value to which the deemed costs percentage is applied.

3.6   Consumables

> **6.   CONSUMABLES**
>
> 6.1.   Consumables include spares for plant and equipment, oil, diesel, sprays, fertilisers, feedstuffs and bags. For any stock of unused, but usable consumables held at the balance sheet date, normally the valuation should be made at cost.
>
> 6.2.   If, however, the consumables have deteriorated or become obsolete then their net realisable value should be used if it is lower than cost.

3.6.1   Seeds, fertilisers, sprays, feeding stuffs, packaging materials, oils, fuels, machinery spares and other consumable stores in stock at the accounting date should be included at actual cost unless the net realisable value would be clearly lower as when they have deteriorated or become obsolete. The time period for the use for particular medicines or chemicals may have expired or their licence withdrawn.

3.6.2   Particular questions over the value to be used can arise at times of price volatility. It is suggested that the cost of purchase should always be used rather than the replacement costs at the balance sheet date, whether prices have moved up or down since purchase.

3.7   Deemed Costs

3.7.1   This section outlines where deemed cost is acceptable and then specifically considers livestock and then harvested crops (headed Deadstock).

> **7.   DEEMED COST VALUATION**
>
> **7.1   When deemed cost is acceptable**
>
> **7.1.1   Valuations should only be based on deemed cost where it is not possible to ascertain actual costs from the farmer's records. Deemed cost should not be used for purchased animals if it is less than the original purchase price plus, if the animal was immature when purchased, the costs of rearing from the date of purchase to the valuation date or, if earlier, to maturity.**
>
> 7.1.2   In such situations Inspectors will accept that a reasonable estimate of cost, "deemed cost", is given by a specific percentage of open market value. It may be necessary, from time to time, to review the percentages if the relationship between costs and market value changes. Current percentages are set out in paragraphs 7.2.1 and 7.3.1 below.
>
> 7.1.3   For production animals open market value should be based on the assumption that there is a willing buyer and a willing seller of the animal as a production animal free from, for example, movement restrictions. It is not acceptable to treat cull value as the open market value of production animals as this does not recognise the value of the future income stream from produce and/or progeny.
>
> **7.2   Livestock**
>
> 7.2.1   The percentages in the case of livestock are
> * cattle - 60% of open market value
> * sheep and pigs - 75% of open market value
>
> 7.2.2.   The following points should be noted:

7.2.3 Deemed cost valuations are only valid for home-bred or home-reared stock or stock acquired some time before maturity and matured on the farm. (See also 7.1.1 above in the case of stock other than home bred stock)

7.2.4 It is preferable for deemed cost to be fixed at maturity but Inspectors will accept valuations at deemed costs based on open market value at the balance sheet date if that method has been used consistently. Farmers should be aware that using deemed cost at each balance sheet date may result in profits coming into tax earlier.

7.2.5 The valuation of immature and unweaned animals using deemed cost methods based on the open market value of animals of a similar age and type is acceptable to the Inland Revenue except in the situation described in paragraph 7.2.6 below. If it is appropriate to value mother and progeny together because that is the market unit, this should be done.

7.2.6. The method at 7.2.5 above is not appropriate where the mother is on the herd basis and where there is no market or a very limited market in unweaned progeny (for example unweaned lambs at foot). In this situation failure to recognise the young stock at all in the valuation is not acceptable. The costs of producing the progeny (see 3.1 above) should be carried forward to be set against the eventual sale price.

7.3. Deadstock (i.e. harvested crops)
7.3.1. Deemed cost based on 75% (85% for valuations as at dates before 31 March 1993) of open market value at the balance sheet date will be accepted by Inspectors.

3.7.2 For four items only, the "deemed cost method" will be acceptable where actual costs are not available. These are:

– harvested (but not growing) crops	75 per cent of market value
– cattle	60 per cent
– sheep	75 per cent
– pigs	75 per cent

being calculated on those prescribed fixed percentages of the market value. These cannot be varied.

3.7.3 Under paragraph 7.2.4 of BEN 19, a deemed cost may be either:
 – fixed at maturity (it would be logical for this to be as at the actual date of maturity); or
 – based on open market value at each accounting period's balance sheet date consistently done.

3.7.4 Cattle, sheep and pigs which are home reared or were purchased young and have been substantially reared by the business can be assessed on deemed costs.

3.7.5 Deemed costs should not be used for animals purchased when already mature and actual costs should be used for them unless their net realisable value is now lower.

3.7.6 Where deemed costs are used for purchased animals under BEN19 7.2.3, it is suggested that they should not usually be less than the actual acquisition cost of the animals in question. Some valuers follow a practice of applying the deemed cost percentage only to the uplift in value over the acquisition cost (so that the stocktaking value is the purchase price of the young stock plus 60 per cent or 75 per cent of the subsequent uplift in value since purchase as it has matured). Others take the acquisition cost and add an allowance for the feed consumed by the animal.

3.7.7   Other stock such as deer, ostriches and alpaca cannot be valued on deemed costs. BIM 55420, Limits to Use of the Deemed Cost Method, stresses that where such method is agreed in an individual case for such stock, it does not constitute a precedent.

3.7.8   BIM 55420 also advises that deemed costs "should not be used where they would not result in a reasonable estimate of cost, for example, for pedigree animals". A pedigree animal may cost little, if anything, more than a commercial animal to rear. A high wheat price could also be an example where the deemed cost percentage would not necessarily result in a reasonable estimate of cost. In such cases, the task is to arrive at that reasonable estimate of cost. This may be easier to do for an arable crop. One practical answer for those livestock where pedigree status brings a higher value might be to apply the deemed cost percentage to the value of an otherwise similar commercial animal.

3.7.9   Once the stocktaking has moved from deemed costs to actual costs, it is not usually possible to return to deemed costs as a method to assess cost.

3.7.10   Valuers should be aware that as deemed costs require an assessment of the market values of the relevant assets, it will be important to show that the same care is taken in assessing this as for other property. This is especially relevant where the Red Book applies with its specified procedures. These issues are discussed further in Chapter 8.

4. THE "MARK-TO-MARKET" OR FAIR VALUE BASIS

4.1   Introduction

4.1.1   While very few businesses engaged in agriculture in the United Kingdom use fair value accounting, this chapter outlines the issues both to assist those valuers who are so instructed and also against a wider application of this approach while this edition is current.

4.1.2   International Accounting Standards (IAS) have been steadily moving towards what might be loosely referred to as a "current value" approach to accounting. Under this approach historic costs are replaced by current values which are to be assessed on the basis of "fair value".

4.1.3   The accounting standards concept of "fair value", perhaps developed to consider the wider range of assets and liabilities (including financial instruments) to be included in accounts is distinct from the definition used in valuation standards. While the valuation definition of fair value is looking at the value of an asset specific to its circumstances, such as the value between two identified parties, the accounting concept is more akin to market value. The definition reads:

> "The price that would be received to sell an asset or paid to transfer a liability in an orderly transaction between willing market participants at the measurement date" (International Accounting Standards Board (IASB), International Financial Reporting Standards (IFRS) 13, para 1.

4.1.4   Despite this approach, the general policy on stocks, as set in IAS2 on Inventories, remains based on the lower of costs and net realisable value. However, IAS 41 adopts a fair value for agricultural crops, livestock and produce (but not other stocks). The Accounting Standard Board's consultation on the extension of IFRS to Small and Medium Enterprises proposes a version of this to agriculture in its Section 34 and the basis of the commentary in this Chapter rather than the more fully fledged IAS 41. The general policy on stocks is at that paper's Section 13.

4.1.5   Should it become recognised as good accountancy practice, then under s.80 of the Finance Act 2005 HMRC would expect tax accounts for relevant businesses to be prepared using it.

4.1.6   At the heart of this approach is a different concept from the traditional approach to profit. In essence, it is looking at the overall change in the overall value of the business in the accounting period between the opening and closing balance sheet dates, not whether its trading activity has made a profit. The argument for this approach may perhaps most easily be made for forestry for which IAS 41 notes that under historic cost forestry might report no income for 30 years even though the business may be becoming more valuable with each year's incremental growth. The argument can seem less relevant to many other crops.

4.1.7   Especially for companies, these standards are applied to accounts through International Financial Reporting Standards (IFRS). EU legislation requires publicly quoted companies to follow IFRS and other entities can follow suit if they choose. This approach has, to date, been excluded for many business (almost all involved in farming) by the UK's Financial Reporting Standards for Small Enterprises (FRSSE).

4.1.8   Potentially Wider Use of Fair Value - However, there is currently a discussion in the UK about applying it "medium enterprises" which would affect the largest businesses involved in farming. Under EU definitions as applied in the United Kingdom (Companies Act, s.382 et seq) a business is a medium-sized one if it meets **two** of three tests, having:

- **a turnover of more than £6.5 million** from sales and services, net of VAT. While there is no statutory definition, it is assumed to exclude investment income and mean operational sales so excluding rents, wayleaves and other non-operational income.
- **a gross balance sheet total of more than £3.26 million** as reported in the balance sheet with fixed assets at book value and current assets (including stocks) as assessed. This figure is not reduced by liabilities such as mortgages. If farmland is held in the accounts at an historic cost it will be that value that is used for this test alongside other assets.
- **more than 50 employees** as assessed on a full time equivalent basis and including owner-managers and business partners.

4.1.9   CAAV analysis suggests this might affect up to 300 businesses with UK farms but these would include many substantial commercial operations. Many more might meet the balance sheet test but large scale, high value farming or an involvement with downstream processing or other activities would be needed to reach either the turnover or the employment tests. Within agriculture, this may be most likely in specialist cropping, fruit, dairy and pig sectors but other businesses may qualify on their own facts.

4.1.10   It is thought that if this happens, there would then be pressure to apply a mark-to-market basis to many smaller businesses.

4.2   Fair Value Approach for Agricultural Stocktaking

4.2.1   This approach would be applied to two classes of stock:
- biological assets, that is, living and growing stocks and so generally growing crops and livestock (the examples in IAS 41 indicate that these include all live animals, whether production animals, progeny or animals that have been bought in)
- agricultural produce, that is the produce of biological assets such as crops in store or wool.

All other items of stock remain on a cost basis under IAS 2.

4.2.2   IAS 41 governs the assessment of stocks for agricultural activity. It defines agricultural activity as "the management by an entity of the biological transformation and harvest of biological assets for sale or for conversion into agricultural produce or into additional biological assets". While covering many things including forestry, that excludes activities outside its scope, such as amenity woodland.

4.2.3   Biological assets (defined by IAS 41 as living animals and plants) are to be valued at each balance sheet date:
- on the fair value basis "where this is readily determinable without undue cost or effort" and
- otherwise on the costs basis.

4.2.4   Agricultural produce (defined by IAS 41 as "the harvested product of the entity's biological assets" and so, for example, harvested grain or fruit) is to be valued at its "fair value" less costs to sell as at the date it was harvested.

4.2.5   The fair value basis for both biological assets and agricultural produce will be its "fair value" as identified for accountancy purposes, less the costs of selling the item.

This approach looks similar to that for net realisable value but would now override costs where it applies.

4.2.6   The approach appears to have a relatively strong bias to finding a "fair value" even where there is no market evidence, as may often be the case for growing crops.

4.2.7   First:
"If an active market exists for a biological asset or agricultural produce in its present location and condition, the quoted price in that market is the appropriate basis for determining the fair value of that asset. If an entity has access to different active markets, the entity shall use the price existing in the market that it expects to use."
That second sentence hints at one of the differences between accountancy's fair value and "market value" but may only rarely be material. An "active market" is defined as one in which:
        – the items traded are homogenous
        – willing buyers and sellers can normally be found at any time
        – prices are available to the public.
The grain markets for wheat or barley might be the best examples within agriculture.

4.2.8   If there is no such current quoted price, then (as under IAS 41) the business is to use:
    (i)   "the most recent market transaction price, provided that there has not been a significant change in economic circumstances between the date of that transaction and the end of the reporting period;
    (ii)   "market prices for similar assets with adjustment to reflect differences; and
    (iii) "sector benchmarks such as the value of an orchard expressed per export tray, bushel, or hectare, and the value of cattle expressed per kilogram of meat."

4.2.9   As it is recognised that these may lead to different values, the approach urges the business (the valuer) to consider:
        "the reasons for those differences, to arrive at the most reliable estimate of fair value within a relatively narrow range of reasonable estimates."

4.2.10   In addition:
        "In some circumstances, fair value may be readily determinable without undue cost or effort even though market determined prices or values are not available for a biological asset in its present condition. An entity shall consider whether the present value of expected net cash flows from the asset discounted at a current market determined rate results in a reliable measure of fair value."

4.2.11   Under this mark-to market approach, such a value has to be found for agricultural produce but it allows that for biological assets a cost basis can instead be used when fair value "is not readily determinable without undue cost or effort". IAS 41 allows that the fair value presumption can be rebutted where the estimates are "clearly unreliable".

4.2.12   The cost basis expects the value to be the item's "cost less any accumulated depreciation and any accumulated impairment losses". In practice, it is assumed that guidance in BEN19 can generally be applied in assessing this.

4.3 Reporting

4.3.1 Where biological assets are valued on a fair value basis, the accounts will need to show the following which generally seem most practically provided by the valuer:

- a description of each class of its biological assets.
- the methods and significant assumptions applied in determining the fair value of each category of agricultural produce at the point of harvest and each category of biological assets.
- a reconciliation of changes in the carrying amount of biological assets between the beginning and the end of the current period. The reconciliation shall include:
  - o the gain or loss arising from changes in fair value less costs to sell
  - o increases resulting from purchases
  - o decreases resulting from harvest
  - o where relevant, increases resulting from business combinations
  - o where relevant, net exchange differences arising on the translation of financial statements into a different presentation currency, and on the translation of a foreign operation into the presentation currency of the reporting entity.
- other changes.

4.3.2 Where the cost basis is used for biological assets, disclosure would be required of:

- a description of each class of its biological assets.
- an explanation of why fair value cannot be measured reliably.
- the depreciation method used.
- the useful lives or the depreciation rates used.
- the gross carrying amount and the accumulated depreciation (aggregated with accumulated impairment losses) at the beginning and end of the period.

4.3.3 No guidance is given as to the requirements for disclosure for agricultural produce which is assumed to remain as now.

4.4 Practical Application

4.4.1 This part of this commentary presents initial views following consideration of IAS 41 and the proposal to extend IFRS to small and medium enterprises. It is likely that it would develop further on more analysis and with practical experience. However, it is offered to assist those valuers who are asked to undertake such stocktakings and as a basis for that future consideration as and when it may be required.

4.4.2 Annual and Short Term Arable Crops - From establishment to harvest they would be biological assets. At this stage, it is generally considered that standing crops will be too difficult to value, except perhaps immediately before harvest. Accordingly, they can usually be assessed on a cost basis.

4.4.3 The produce once harvested will be "agricultural produce". The date of that separation is the valuation date for agricultural produce. The "fair value" at that date is applied to stock still in store at the balance sheet date. However, if the value has fallen since it may be possible to revalue downwards.

4.4.4 This analysis suggests that a move to a fair value approach would see
- most crops in the ground remain on the same basis
- harvested crops move from being assessed on cost to market value.

4.4.5   Where harvested crops have been assessed on a deemed costs basis, they would now be at market value, assessed at point of harvest, though if the market value at the balance sheet date is lower, an adjustment can be made to that figure. Whether moving from actual cost or deemed cost, the value of harvested crops in stocks would thus rise.

4.4.6   Further consideration would need to be given to what is meant by the point of harvest. Is that when:
     – the product is separated from the biological asset
     – it is put into store?
IAS 41 says it does not deal with the processing of agricultural produce after harvest but the examples given are of turning grapes into wine or wool into yarn.

4.4.7   The point can be illustrated by reference to:
     – silage – is it grass as cut in the swath or silage after it has passed through the forage harvester and been ensiled?
     – grain – in a poor year is it wet grain from the field or grain in store as dried and cleaned for storage and sale?
There will often be much more evidence of the values of the produce as stored for sale or use than as cut, while values for produce exactly as severed might generally be much lower. If severance is indeed to be the point of valuation, are the costs of ensiling or drying/cleaning then to be added to the market value of the agricultural products when valuing the stocks?

4.4.8   The practicalities of evidence may mean that different answers will be found for different cases. It might usually be that there is more evidence for grain sold off the combine than for grass in the swath. It assumes that appropriate records have been kept of what was harvested as the harvest unfolded. With often very limited or negligible direct evidence, the valuation of silage in the clamp has long been an area of professional debate.

4.4.9   Where a harvested crop has been partially sold or used at the balance sheet date, there may need to be assumptions as to which stocks have been sold or used – last in first out, first in first out, or averaging?

4.4.10 Medium Term (Say, 2 to 7 Year) Crops - At this stage, the same analysis appears to acceptable.

4.4.11 One issue, especially for horticulture and nursery work, is the approach to biological assets. An asparagus crown or strawberry plant, being grown to yield produce to be harvested from it, will be a biological asset and probably incapable of being assessed at fair value. However, there are plants grown for onward sale - roses, shrubs, bedding plants, miscanthus rhizomes, etc - which remain biological assets but will usually have a sale value at any point – since the plant itself is the object of the enterprise.

4.4.12 Another issue is whether, given the often substantial costs of establishment, there should be depreciation of biological assets such as fruit bushes over their life.

4.4.13 Long Term Crops (Orchards, Vines, Forestry) - There may be a distinction to be drawn (perhaps by the valuer in determining whether a fair value can be assessed) between those plants that are the produce themselves (trees for timber) and those that are managed for their produce (apple orchard or vineyard). The former may generally be capable of "fair value" with evidence of, say, the timber value and costs to sale, more or less readily to hand. The latter, having no existence apart from the land in which they are rooted and not sold separately from the land, may not be capable of such a valuation.

4.4.14   In the absence of a market, the valuation of, say, an orchard on the basis of its future yield and costs is simply too speculative – fair value cannot be assessed reliably. Yield and quality are heavily influenced by the chance of weather and disease. Future market prices are unknown and may be lower or higher than at the valuation date – the same will be true of costs. Depressed prices could simply make picking uneconomic as may issues in the labour market.

4.4.15   The depreciation point also arises.

4.4.16   Livestock - Where no slaughter takes place within the business, livestock may always be "biological assets" - so, for example, lambs and other progeny might still be included at net "fair value" as at the balance sheet date, because they remain alive. Items such as milk and wool would be "agricultural produce". A move to a fair value basis might see a greater demand for annual valuations on livestock farms.

4.4.17   The valuer may need to identify the valuation units - as where lambs or calves at foot would be sold with the dam rather than separately.

4.4.18   This would see almost all stock accounted for at market value rather than cost, whether that cost is directly assessed or reached by a deemed cost calculation. Either way it seems likely that the transition would see an uplift in value. Where cattle are currently assessed to deemed cost at 60 per cent of market value that would see an uplift of two-thirds.

4.4.19   Of itself, a move to market value does not override the statutory herd basis (though it might throw it into question). However, and while it remains, there might have to be a further computation in working from the accounts to the tax return to exclude the market value of the breeding animals in the production herd.

4.4.20   Particular consideration would have to be given to breeding sows in intensive high health status pig units as their only market value is often a cull value.

4.4.21   It is likely that animals reared on long term contracts would be considered separately.

4.4.22   The move from cost to net fair value may see a particular uplift for specialist breeding stock where their market value reflects the anticipated income stream from them. Purely as a more extreme indication, a young bull reared for breeding and perceived to have a high potential was valued on appeal in 2001 at towards £1.5 million – almost all of that value would be uplift over cost.

4.4.23   Grants and Subsidies - While there can be differing views now about when government grants are to be recognised, Section 24 of IFRS for SMEs Section 24 seems clear that this should only be done when the grant is fully due. Were this to be followed through, it would make accounts more volatile and less like cash flow while perhaps increasing the overall tax burden for some taxpayers through the interaction with progressive tax bands. That raises concerns over multi-annual schemes - such as many five and ten year agri-environment agreements – for which this condition may not be satisfied until sometime after the end of the agreement. Payments with interest can be recovered during the scheme should it be breached or abandoned. Issues may arise where changes in land occupation require a new calculation of points or in some circumstances with CAP reform. It may be that if the income is deferred so too should be the associated costs.

4.4.24   As these accumulated concerns might suggest that some practical resolution would be found as it became needed, it is probably pointless to pursue the speculation further. In the meantime any valuers confronted with this issue should discuss the approach with the client's accountant.

4.4.25   Stud Farms - Where a stud farm is brought onto a mark-to-market basis for stocktaking, the horses are likely to be biological assets and so assessed at their market value less costs to sale. While there are relatively deep and liquid markets for many (but not all) types and breeds of farm livestock, valuations of horses in stud farms may often be more subjective while the fragile and unpredictable nature of horses also adds an element of risk not present for or so pertinent for many other animals. Fashion, racing results and many other factors can all move values significantly between years. If all such horses are to be held on the balance sheet at their valuation, this subjectivity will be applied to a larger proportion of total assets.

4.4.26   However, it is probably not possible in most cases to argue that such valuations could not be achieved without undue cost or effort. Such valuations are currently necessary for transfers of horses between breeding and racing businesses in the same ownership. The valuations would, by the nature of the animals, simply be less secure and less stable.

4.4.27   At some point, there may be an issue as to whether value can be measured reliably. Where there is recent evidence from arm's length sales of live animals relevant to the animal in question, the reliability of the valuation would be seen to be greater. That would also suggest that the nearer a typical animal is to market at a year end, the easier it might be to form a view as to its value. In such cases, adjustments would need to be made to reflect the characteristics of the animal in question.

4.4.28   Breeding stallions, like breeding bulls, might perhaps often be more appropriately valued by reference to future income stream expected at the valuation date, discounting that to a capital value.

4.4.29   Post-balance sheet date knowledge, especially of sales and possibly of medical events, may often be particularly pertinent in maintaining realism.

4.4.30   Unborn progeny are currently valued at nomination cost unless there is either a free nomination or a foal-share agreement, when they are typically held at nil cost. If a pregnant mare is valued at fair value then this might be expected to include an element for the value of the unborn foal that she carries, thus there would be no separation at that point.

4.4.31   The foal might be regarded as a separate valuation unit either once born or after weaning (which might be in a different accounting year).

4.4.32   Managing the New System – Where issues raised by a move to fair value are significant, some farmers may consider changing their year end, perhaps especially where the business is devoted to enterprises with a predictable annual production cycle.

5. TREATMENT OF LONG TERM CONTRACTS

5.1   Specific rules apply under SSAP 9 for accounting treatment of long term contracts as may, for example, be found for specialist seed potato growing. This is distinct from the question of the choice of basis for stocktaking between costs and fair value.

5.2   The position on work on contracts generally in the context of stock is set out by HMRC at BIM 33020 which says:
> "Except where they are long term contracts (see BIM33025), uncompleted contracts for services should be valued at their cost so that a profit or loss is not recognised for tax purposes until the contractual obligations required have been completed."

5.3   Long term contracts are defined in SSAP9 Part 2, paragraph 22 as:
> "A contract entered into for the design, manufacture or construction of a single substantial asset or the provision of a service (or of a combination of assets or services which together constitute a single project) where the time taken substantially to complete the contract is such that the contract activity falls into different accounting periods. A contract that is required to be accounted for as long-term by this accounting standard will usually extend for a period exceeding one year. However, a duration exceeding one year is not an essential feature of a long-term contract. Some contracts with a shorter duration than one year should be accounted for as long-term contracts if they are sufficiently material to the activity of the period that not to record turnover and attributable profit would lead to a distortion of the period's turnover and results such that the financial statements would not give a true and fair view, provided that the policy is applied consistently within the reporting entity and from year to year."

5.4   The key points seem to be that:
– the activity under the contract falls into more than one accounting period
– it will often be for more than one year
– shorter contracts may still be "long term contracts" where not recording turnover and attributable profit would distort the view of the accounts in which case the policy must be applied consistently from year to year.

5.5   HMRC's guidance on this subject is that "Profits and losses recognised during the currency of long term contracts are recognised for tax purposes" (BIM 33025).

5.6   HMRC gives a little more guidance at BIM 33155 on valuing long term contracts
> "The basic principles are given in paragraphs 21 to 27 in SSAP9.
>
> "SSAP9 requires the accrual of attributable profit into long-term contract values but it does not give detailed guidance on how the amount is actually to be computed."

5.7   Paragraph 23 of SSAP9 states:
> "Attributable profit: that part of the total profit currently estimated to arise over the duration of the contract, after allowing for estimated remedial and maintenance costs and increases in costs so far as not recoverable under the terms of the contract, that fairly reflects the profit attributable to that part of the

work performed at the accounting date. (There can be no attributable profit until the profitable outcome of the contract can be assessed with reasonable certainty.)"

5.8 This means that the income on "long term contracts" must be accounted for over the period of the contract as the profits are earned. This is only tempered by the question of whether the attributable profit can be assessed with reasonable certainty as at the balance sheet date. The test here is a judgment of reasonable certainty, not a guarantee. Where income due under a "long term contract" cannot be assessed with reasonable certainty at the balance sheet date it should not be recognised and so the matching costs (or the fair value of the crops) would then be put into stocks.

6. HERD BASIS

Note – This section is not a detailed manual to the herd basis, just a basic description as it touches on stocktaking concerns.

6.1   Livestock (including shares in animals – BIM55445) kept for farming purposes are, in principle, trading stock (ITTOIA, s.30).

6.2   However, a farmer who is treated by HMRC as carrying on trade (ITTOIA s.9) and who has livestock which forms part of a "production herd or flock" can elect for the *herd basis* to apply to that herd or flock. If he does so, then that basis will apply instead of the trading stock basis (for partners and sole traders, see ITTOIA, Part 2, Chapter 8 from s.111; for companies, see the Corporation Tax Act 2009) for tax purposes only. This election may only be made within specified time limits and circumstances. Once made, it is irrevocable.

6.3   Paragraph 8(6) of that Schedule states that production herds are of the same class if they are of the same species. This means that an election cannot be made, for example, just for the Hereford production herd but not the Simmental one – the election will apply to all cattle kept in production herds by that farmer.

6.4   The herd basis only applies to production animals, kept for their produce (such as milk, eggs, or offspring) and not for sale themselves. Female animals may not enter the "herd" until they have given birth. Related progeny are not eligible for inclusion even if unweaned, save in certain exceptions for hill sheep.

6.5   The effect is that the "herd" is generally treated as though it is a capital asset with the costs of maintaining the herd chargeable against tax and any profit on the final disposal of the herd will not be liable to tax.

6.6   The herd basis is considered in greater detail by HMRC's Help Sheet HS224 – see Annexe J.

6.7   Animals Still to be in Stocktaking - A production herd accounted for on the herd basis is often treated for tax purposes as though it were a fixed asset and need not be valued for stocktaking purposes. Reconciliations should, however, be maintained to establish transfers in and out of the herd, distinguishing the home bred and bought-in animals.

6.8   Unweaned progeny of herd basis animals will not be on the herd basis and so should be directly accounted for in stocktaking. The deemed cost basis for unweaned progeny maybe less appropriate when a normal valuation unit is the mother and the progeny taken together, since any assessment of market value from deemed cost may, in some cases, be based on poor or artificial market evidence. Where this is so, actual cost should be used for such progeny.

6.9   Checklist - If the farmer has elected to use the Herd Basis, the accountant will require the following information for the herd basis:
          – opening number by categories
          – purchases by category and the year
          – transfers into the herd in the year
          – sales by category in the year
          – deaths in the year
If necessary, this may be cross-checked with the animal movement book.

6.10   Where a limited company has a production herd, the accountant may still require a value for animals held on the herd basis, even though this is irrelevant for tax purposes.

7. INSTRUCTIONS AND REPORTING

Note - Valuers subject to RICS regulations are also referred to the requirements of the RICS Red Book regarding terms of engagement and reporting which are reviewed in Chapter 8. The RICS is expected to produce an Information Paper shortly on the application of the Red Book's requirements to farm stocktakings.

7.1 General

7.1.1 The figures produced should assist the accountant in preparing the accounts and the farmer in completing his tax return.

7.1.2 HMRC Self Assessment Help Sheet 224 (now on reference HS224 and most recently issued in 2012) for Farmers and Market Gardeners suggests that when completing the tax return it will be helpful if, in addition to the total figure for the stocktaking, a note is attached breaking it down by categories:

> "There is only space to enter a single figure for stock in box 84 of your *Self-employment (full)* pages or box 3.101 of your Partnership Tax Return. You may provide a breakdown of that figure in the 'Any other information' box, box 102. Providing this information with your tax return may help avoid enquiries."

The latest edition now simply refers back to Helpsheet 232 (BEN 19) for further detail.

7.1.3 In the case of a farm account which is selected for enquiry by HMRC, the taxpayer may well be called upon to produce details of physical reconciliations as well as justifying the figures that he has included for actual cost or deemed cost as may be appropriate.

7.2 Terms of Engagement

7.2.1 The terms of engagement will generally both formalise in writing the instructions necessary to undertake the stocktaking and the valuer's terms of business. They will also clarify who is the client and, perhaps useful for a company or partnership, who is the point of contact. It would also be useful to have the client's confirmation of the identity of the accountant but this might usually be outside the terms of engagement.

7.2.2 As they are most easily drafted by the valuer, they should be sent to the client with a copy for him to sign and return to record the contract for the work. A sample template is offered at Annexe A.

7.2.3 For an annual task such as stocktaking where there is an expectation that the valuer will be repeatedly instructed, it will be practical to express the terms of engagement as a standing instruction so that it will operate by default unless rescinded by either party or varied by agreement.

7.2.4 If there are any potential or actual conflicts of interest, the manner in which these are to be dealt with should be addressed.

7.2.5 Instructions – This part of the terms of engagement can be written as instructions as to the purpose of the valuation, the basis of valuation and procedure.

7.2.6 The typical instruction would be to provide an annual stocktaking to use in accounts prepared for the client's tax return. Where relevant, a reference may be made to audit purposes. The balance sheet date will be the valuation date.

7.2.7   The subject of the valuation would, as relevant, be the interest of the client in:
- growing crops and cultivations (including seeds, fertilisers and chemicals applied and beneficial acts of husbandry)
- harvested crops and produce
- farm livestock (potentially excluding any that are on the herd basis),
- deadstock (including but not restricted to seeds, fertilisers, chemicals, fuels and oils, animal feeds).

The sample terms of engagement at Annexe A refer to the interest to be valued as "Relevant assets owned, held or available for use by the business". This recognises that there may be stocks on the farm, perhaps even already applied to growing crops, for which title may not yet have passed to the farming business. The physical stocks exist on the farm and would be matched by a corresponding creditor just as crops in store would be valued at the balance sheet date even if subject to a forward sale or included in a merchant's pool for which an advance payment may have been made.

7.2.8   Save where, unusually, the fair value basis has been adopted, the basis of valuation would be cost (including deemed cost) or, if lower, net realisable value. The instructions could require that the valuation will be undertaken in accordance with SSAP9 and HMRC's HS232 (previously BEN19) and have regard to the CAAV Guidance Notes on Agricultural Stock Valuations for Tax Purposes and, where necessary, RICS Valuation – Professional Standards (the Red Book). No allowance will be made for any taxation liability (whether actual or notional) which may arise on the disposal of stock.

7.2.9   Valuers can use the letter of engagement to outline the information required from the client and his other advisers as well as to set out the scope of inspection and investigation that is expected. It can define the extent of any reconciliation expected of the valuer. It may be that the client will be expected to provide any necessary reconciliation of physical quantities.

7.2.10   It is often prudent to record certain assumptions that are likely to be made. These might include:
- the assets to be valued are owned by the client
- deadstocks are in useable condition
- livestock is free from disease
- harvested crops are fit for market

as well stating that the information supplied by the client as to the ownership, description, quantities and condition of items is assumed to be correct and that there are no undisclosed matters that would affect the valuation.

7.2.11   The valuer can then reserve his position so that he may alter his opinion as of value should it be established subsequently that any information provided was incorrect.

7.2.12   The instructions can also be used to limit potential liabilities by recording that the report is only to be used for the instructed purpose and only by the client to whom it is confidential so that it may not be published without consent (save as it has to be used in the statutorily published accounts of a company or a limited liability partnership).

7.2.13 The Terms of Business – These are likely to be individual to the valuer or the practice and should include details as to the basis of the fee. If the terms of engagement have be drafted as a standing instruction, care needs to be taken here to allow for normal business changes, such as in fee rates.

7.2.14   Once specific points such as the fee (or the fee basis) have been set out, it may then often be simplest to refer to and attach the firm's general Terms of Business which may, among other matters, cover:
 – billing arrangements
 – the practice's complaints procedure.

7.2.15   The fee can expressed as being either:
 – on a time and expenses basis, whether recording specific figures or just advising the client of current rates
 – a fixed charge with or without expenses or any charge for additional work.
The VAT treatment should be stated.

7.2.16   The method for ending the instruction should be set out with any accompanying practicalities.

7.3   The Valuation

7.3.1   Most of the practical points in actually undertaking the stocktaking have been covered elsewhere in this paper as the text relates to the information that is to be sought, checked, recorded and inspected to enable the physical quantities and values to be reviewed for the report.

7.3.2   Valuations undertaken before the end of the accounting period will need supplementary information to be complete. If this reconciliation is to be done by the accountant, he needs to be able to see clearly from the stocktaking what has already been taken into account.

7.3.3   An issue may arise over deliveries late in the accounting period as physical delivery may usually be the point at which indebtedness arises, irrespective of the invoice point. The accountant may ask for a value of a list of stocks for which payment has not been made (to be creditors in the accounts). The valuer will need to check that paperwork is moved in sympathy with the goods and so may need to see invoices for goods. Particular care will need to be taken with those goods (such as sprays) which may have been used before the inspection. Deliveries made after the end of the accounting period do not form part of the stocktaking.

7.4   Report on the Stocktaking

7.4.1   The report on the stocktaking, addressed to the client, will set out the stocktaking, its assumptions and qualifications. It is the valuer's opportunity to be clear, identifying what he has seen and done, his sources of information and his approach, so protecting himself. A sample template for the stocktaking is offered at Annexe B. Each practice should consider the form of its report in the light of its client base and the standards it sets for stocktaking. Those practices that are regulated by the RICS will need to consider the requirements of the Red Book which are reviewed in Chapter 8.

7.4.2   The valuer should state the purpose of the stocktaking and its intended use. The valuer should set out any limitations in his report to define the extent of his liability.

7.4.3   In many valuations, the valuer relies on information from the client. Where this is the case, this should be disclosed in the report. If a valuer is unhappy with the integrity of the valuation or the information available, then it may be prudent not to issue a certificate but to inform the client or accountant of his reservations.

7.4.4   The valuer should set out the basis or bases of valuation used whether generally or by categories:
 – actual costs and whether or not using CAAV costs with or without adjustment
 – deemed costs
 – net realisable value.
Where a fair value approach is taken that should be clearly stated together with any exceptions adopted where the effort or uncertainty in identifying fair value would be disproportionate to the benefit to the client.

7.4.5   Where a costs basis is used the valuer should show the figure that represents any element of depreciation in the stocktaking so that the adjustments required for the tax computation can be undertaken.

7.4.6   He should give his opinion on the amount to be included for stock by categories as appropriate.

7.4.7   Notes should be attached to show any reconciliation of numbers for the herd basis.

7.5   Afterwards
7.5.1   The valuer should retain all his detailed working papers leading to the valuation so that he can answer all questions should there be an enquiry by HMRC. Such enquiries can often start with a consideration of the stocktaking valuation.

7.5.2   Notes should be retained for any work done on:
 – crop reconciliations
 – details of home saved seed
 – net realisable value calculations
 – livestock numbers and details
and any extent to which subsidies are included.

8. VALUATION STANDARDS AND PRACTICE

8.1   In addition to the requirements of statute law, clients, and accounting standards, the valuation profession has developed both valuation standards and guidance on practice to encourage consistency in good practice to the benefit of clients and the profession.

8.2   The CAAV

8.2.1   The CAAV publishes texts such as this one to offer briefing to members to support and disseminate good practice and benefit discussion of professional issues. It also uses its website, the News Letter, conferences and other means to these ends.

8.2.2   CAAV members are anyway bound by the CAAV's Bylaws on professional conduct which address professional conduct generally with no specific points as to stocktaking work. These include Bylaws 5.1 and 5.2:

5.1.   Members shall in all points of their business conduct themselves professionally and with probity.

5.2.   Each member shall conduct his professional work by:
   (i)   discharging his duties with due care, attention and competence
   (ii)   conducting himself with diligence, honesty and integrity
   (iii) exercising his professional judgement objectively
   (iv)   being open and accountable to clients in these matters
   (v)   upholding and demonstrating these professional standards in his work, demonstrating his integrity so as to maintain the reputation of the Association.

8.2.3   In addition, Fellows are required by:
   – Bylaw 5.3(a) to advise clients in writing when a conflict of interest arises in the course of an instruction,
   – Bylaw 5.3(c) to keep themselves abreast of all professional matters and current developments relevant to their professional work

They are also required to carry appropriate Professional indemnity cover and have a complaints procedure.

8.3   Valuation Standards

8.3.1   Valuation standards are prepared and issued by a number of professional organisations around the world. These include:
   – International Valuation Standards issued by the International Valuation Standards Council and now adopted by the RICS
   – European Valuation Standards issued by the European Group of Valuers Associations (TEGoVA).

8.3.2   These typically outline core definitions of bases of value (such as market value), and standards for mattes such as the qualification of valuers and reporting together with commentaries on applying those standards and other information.

8.3.3   European Valuation Standards - EVS (latest edition 2012 – the Blue Book)) concerns the valuation of real property rather than personal property and so is not directly relevant to agricultural stocktaking. However, the general observations of standards EVS 3 (the Qualified Valuer), EVS 4 (the Valuation Process), and EVS 5 (Reporting the Valuation) will be relevant.

8.3.4   International Valuation Standards - The main focus of IVS (latest edition 2011 – commonly, the White Book) is now broader than real property, explaining the shift in the focus of the definition of market value from property to assets and liabilities. The RICS has adopted this as part of adopting International Valuation Standards rather than setting its own.

8.3.5   In GN10, Valuation of Agricultural Properties which was issued with IVS 2007, it drew attention to IAS41 but as discussed above this is unlikely to apply to most farm stocktakings in the United Kingdom. However, its general expectations of the valuer and the valuation process will be relevant. It was not carried forward into IVS 2011 as it was considered that it "contained no requirements that differed from those for other real property types".

8.4   RICS Regulation

8.4.1   This bears on agricultural stocktakings both through the Red Book and the RICS Valuer Registration Scheme. As most members of the CAAV are RICS members or in RICS regulated practices, these requirements are now considered. It should be noted that the RICS is expected shortly to produce an Information Paper offering guidance on the requirements of the Red Book as they relate to agricultural stocktakings.

8.4.2   RICS Valuer Registration Scheme - RICS rules now provide that the only RICS members (or people within RICS regulated practices) who can be responsible for stocktakings are those registered with it under the RICS Valuer Registration Scheme. This has no force beyond those circumstances but does mean that in a practice that is regulated by the RICS the stocktaking must be signed off by an RICS Registered Valuer for that practice to be compliant with the RICS.

8.4.3   Those stocktakings are then to be undertaken in accordance with the Red Book which at VS 1.6 requires the valuer to be appropriately trained, have appropriate experience and the time and resources to undertake the work.

8.4.4   The RICS requires that in an RICS regulated practice:
– any valuer who carries out a material part of the valuation is to be registered with its scheme and
– where work on the stocktaking is done by valuers who are not RICS qualified, the RICS registered valuer must be sufficiently involved to be able to sign the report.

8.5   Application of the RICS Red Book

8.5.1   On the argument that the valuation of farm stock is the valuation of assets, the RICS Red Book has for many years applied to stocktaking though this has not been widely recognised.

8.5.2   VS 1.1.5 sets out the circumstances where VS 2 to VS 6 do not apply. In practice, these concern advice during negotiations or potential litigation. The RICS considers that as a stocktaking is generally used to assist a statutory tax return the Red Book applies.

8.5.3   Valuers who are RICS members should refer to Red Book Practice Statement UKVS 1.14, *Trading Stock*. This requires assets held as trading stock and work in progress to be valued in accordance with Statement of Standard Accounting Practice 9 (SSAP9 published by the Accounting Standards Board) and so at cost or, if lower, net realisable value.

8.5.4   UKVS 1.14 quotes the ASB's definition in SSAP9 of net realisable value as "the actual or estimated selling price (net of trade but before settlement discounts) less.
i.   all further costs to completion, and
ii. all costs to be incurred in marketing, selling and distributing."

8.5.5   UKVS 1.14 mostly addresses building and development work (where land and buildings may more often be stock in trade). However, at paragraph 7 it expressly refers RICS members to BEN19 for agricultural stocktakings. At paragraph 6, it excludes farming stock valuations from the requirement to obtain written statements from the client setting out costs to date and to be incurred as at the valuation date.

8.5.6   The Red Book has thus adopted the conventional approach to stocktaking. Nonetheless, since deemed costs are derived from market values the RICS requires that the IVS definition of market value as now adopted by the Red Book at VS 3.2 is stated and applied with the accompanying requirements. This IVS definition reads:
"the estimated amount for which an asset or liability should exchange on the valuation date between a willing buyer and a willing seller in an arm's length transaction, after proper marketing and where the parties had each acted knowledgeably, prudently and without compulsion."

8.5.7   That will mean that the valuer will need to record on the file the supporting comparable evidence against a possible future need to justify the figures assessed.

8.5.8   With that exception, the burden of the Red Book lies in regulation of process, as with terms of engagement and reporting.

8.5.9   VS 1.7 requires the valuer to identify and deal with any actual or potential conflict of interest and record it on the file.

8.5.10 Terms of Engagement - The valuer's terms of engagement by the client are to comply with VS 2. They are to be in writing and at the least cover the following points:
– identification of the client and any other intended users;
– the purpose of the valuation;
– the subject of the valuation;
– the interest to be valued;
– the type of asset or liability and how it is used or classified by the client;
– the basis, or bases, of value;
– the valuation date;
– disclosure of any material involvement, or a statement that there has not been any previous material involvement;
– the identity of the valuer responsible for the valuation and, if required, a statement of the status of the valuer;
– where appropriate, the currency to be adopted;
– any assumptions, special assumptions, reservations, special instructions or departures;
– the extent of the valuer's investigations;
– the nature and source of the information to be relied on by the valuer;
– any consent to, or restrictions on, publication;
– any limits or exclusion of liability to parties other than the client;
– confirmation that the valuation will be undertaken in accordance with the Red Book and that it also complies with the International Valuation Standards, where appropriate;

- confirmation that the valuer has the knowledge, skills and understanding to undertake the valuation competently;
- the basis on which the fee will be calculated;
- where the firm is registered for regulation by RICS, reference to the firm's complaints handling procedure, with a copy available on request; and
- a statement that compliance with these standards may be subject to monitoring under the RICS' conduct and disciplinary regulations.

8.5.11   The terms of engagement are the place to record any instructions by the client to depart from the Red Book or to make any assumptions which should then also be recorded in the report.

8.5.12   As farm stocktakings are seen to be but one example of a valuation under the Red Book, the RICS asks the valuer to establish from the farmer's accountant the purpose of the valuation and what accounting standards apply to this. Those standards are to be agreed with the accountant, recorded in the file, stated in the terms of engagement, used for the valuation and set out in the report.

8.5.13   The Report - The report on the stocktaking is to comply with VS 6. VS 6.1 requires all valuation reports to be:
- clear and unambiguous to the reader and
- prepared with high standards of integrity, clarity and objectivity.

8.5.14   The RICS' minimum requirements for a valuation report to do that at VS 6.1.
- identification of the client and any other intended users;
- the purpose of the valuation;
- the subject of the valuation;
- the interest to be valued;
- the type of asset or liability and how it is used, or classified, by the client;
- the basis, or bases, of value;
- the valuation date;
- disclosure of any material involvement, or a statement that there has not been any previous material involvement;
- the identity of the valuer responsible for the valuation and, if required, a statement of the status of the valuer;
- where appropriate, the currency that has been adopted;
- any assumptions, special assumptions, reservations, special instructions or departures;
- the extent of the valuer's investigations;
- the nature and source of information relied on by the valuer;
- any consent to, or restrictions on, publication;
- any limits or exclusion of liability to parties other than the client;
- confirmation that the valuation accords with the Red Book and that it also complies with the International Valuation Standards, where appropriate;
- a statement of the valuation approach and reasoning;
- a statement that the valuer has the knowledge, skills and understanding to undertake the valuation competently;
- the opinions of value in figures and words;
- signature and date of the report.

8.5.15   At VS 6.2, the RICS requires that the valuation must not be referred to as a "certificate of value" or "valuation certificate" as these terms have meanings elsewhere.

ANNEXE A

SAMPLE TEMPLATE FOR TERMS OF ENGAGEMENT

This model agreement is intended to be just that: a help to members preparing their own agreements. The agreement will need to be tailored to suit necessary individual circumstances and sound local practices. The adaptation of this agreement to practical circumstances is a matter for the professional judgement of members for which the CAAV can accept no liability.

Note – This template is drafted for valuations on the basis of the lower of cost and net realisable value. It would need to be revised where a valuation is to be on the basis of fair value.

Dear Sir,

Annual Stocktaking Valuation

We are pleased to confirm your standing instructions to undertake an annual valuation of your farm stock for stocktaking purposes and write to confirm our terms of business. Please read this letter and the attached terms of business carefully and retain them for your future reference.

Client

[Business name and address of client]

Contact

[Contact name and number]

Instructions

Your instructions are to provide you with an annual stocktaking valuation for the above-named business. Additions and variations to these instructions may be agreed between us from time to time. Any significant additions or variations will be confirmed in writing.

Purpose of Valuation
For use in the preparation of annual accounts [and for audit purposes] *(as appropriate)*.

Subject of Valuation
Where applicable, farm livestock (excluding any which will be on the herd basis), deadstock (including but not restricted to seeds, fertilisers, chemicals, fuels and oils, animal feeds, harvested crops and produce) and growing crops and cultivations (including seeds, fertilisers and chemicals applied and beneficial acts of husbandry).

Interest to be valued
Relevant assets owned, held or available for use by the business.

Basis of Valuation
Stocks will be valued on the basis of cost or, if lower, net realisable value.

The valuation will be undertaken in accordance with SSAP9 and HMRC's HS23? (previously BEN19), will comply with RICS Valuation – Professional Standards and wil have regard to the CAAV Guidance Notes on Agricultural Stock Valuations for Ta> Purposes.

Taxation
No allowance will be made for any taxation liability (whether actual or notional) whicl may arise on the disposal of stock.

Grants & Subsidies
No account of any grants or subsidies will be taken (except as expressly instructed or a! required for net realisable value).

Date of Valuation
Day/Month in any year

Name and Status of Valuer
The valuation will be carried out by [name and qualifications of valuer], RIC! Registered Valuer and Fellow/Probationer of the Central Association of Agricultura Valuers (CAAV). The valuer has sufficient current local and national knowledge of the market, and the skills and understanding to undertake the valuation competently, and wil act as an External Valuer.

Statement of Material Involvement (Conflict of Interest)
[name of valuer] has undertaken previous stocktaking valuations for the client and ha! an ongoing fee earning relationship with the client. [change if first valuation for client As far as we are aware there is no conflict of interest that would prevent the Valuer o the Firm from accepting and undertaking these instructions with the required objectivity Or
We are aware of [insert details of potential conflict of interest] which may potentiall result in a conflict of interest. [However, we have [insert details of steps taken to negate conflict of interest] which we consider is sufficient to negate the potential conflict o interest] Or [However, we have discussed this and you have confirmed that you are happy for me to act for you in this matter].

Currency
The valuation will be stated in pounds sterling.

Assumptions
Unless we have been advised or have ascertained otherwise from our inspection, the following assumptions (which we shall be under no duty to verify) will be made in respect of stock items:
(a) the assets to be valued are owned or contracted to be purchased by the client
(b) deadstocks are in useable condition
(c) livestock is free from disease
(d) growing crops are fully established and in reasonable condition for their growth stage
(e) harvested crops are fit for market.

We will assume that the information supplied to us as to ownership, description quantities and condition of stock items is correct and that there are no undisclosed matters that would affect our valuation. However, should it be established subsequently that any information provided to us was incorrect, this might alter our opinion of value from that reported.

Extent of Investigations

Unless agreed otherwise we will carry out such investigations as we consider appropriate for the valuation including a brief inspection of such stocks as we consider appropriate for the valuation. We will not verify the legal ownership of any stocks nor verify quantities unless specifically requested to do so.

Nature and Sources of Information

Unless expressly agreed otherwise, we will rely on such information as to stocks to be valued as is given to us by the client and/or the client's employees or professional advisers. Where we consider that information being relied upon needs to be verified by further checks, we will advise accordingly.

Limitation of Liability

The valuation report will be provided for the stated purpose(s) and for the sole use of the named client. It will be confidential to the client and his/her professional advisors and we will not accept any responsibility whatsoever to any other person in respect of the whole or any part of its contents. The valuation may not be used for any other purpose.

Consent to Publication

Neither the whole nor any part of the valuation report or any reference thereto may be included in any document, circular or statement or published in any way, without our prior written approval of the form and context in which it may appear, save as to meet statutory obligations except that the information included herein may be used in published accounts of the client/business.

[RICS Regulation

This firm/valuer is regulated by Royal Institution of Chartered Surveyors (RICS), registration number [insert number]. The valuation will be carried out in accordance with the current edition of RICS Valuation – Professional Standards and may be investigated by the RICS for the purposes of ensuring compliance with these standards.]

CAAV

The Valuer is subject the professional standards of the Central Association of Agricultural Valuers (CAAV).

Accountant

We will liaise with your accountant as necessary in order to produce the valuation and provide them with a copy of the valuation or provide you with an additional copy of the valuation for them. Our records indicate that your accountant is [accountant's name and address] but if this is not the case then please let me know immediately.

Responsibilities

You agree to provide all necessary information required by us to complete the valuation.

The person with day to day conduct of this matter is [insert name], (assisted by other staff as required) and he/she will be your main point of contact. The job will be overseen by [insert name], who is the partner with overall responsibility. We will try to avoid changing the personnel working on this matter, but if this cannot be avoided we will inform you of the new job manager or partner as appropriate.

Fees Basis and Payment

[Our fees will be on a time and expenses basis, calculated mainly by reference to the time spent by partners and staff dealing with the matter, including travelling time where appropriate. The current hourly rates for each member of staff that apply to this job are set out in the attached schedule.] OR

[Our fees will be at the agreed fixed sum of £X,XXX [plus] [inclusive of] disbursements and expenses [estimated at £XXX]. If additional work is required to that originally agreed or if the scope of the job is wider than originally envisaged, we shall charge an additional fee to be agreed between us or in default of agreement charged on a time basis in accordance with our standard hourly rates as set out in the attached schedule/which will be supplied to you on request.]

VAT will be added to fees and expenses at the appropriate rate.

We will account to you on completion of the valuation but reserve the right to submit an interim account after 6 months and 3-monthly thereafter should this matter not be completed within 6 months.

Complaints

This firm operates a formal complaints procedure, a copy of which is available on request.

Termination

You may terminate these instructions on written notice at any time but please note that where we are bound to fulfil any obligations to third parties even after termination of your instructions, we will do so and reserve the right to charge for the time spent and any costs incurred.

We may terminate our agreement to act on your instructions on giving you reasonable written notice taking into account all the relevant circumstances and our professional obligations. We reserve the right to terminate our instructions immediately in the event of:
(a) Any overdue accounts;
(b) A receiving order being made against you or if a meeting of your creditors is called or if you are adjudicated bankrupt or if the Client (being a company) enters into compulsory or voluntary liquidation;
(c) Failure to provide information reasonably required by us to undertake the work;
(d) Conflict of interest.

Should you terminate our instructions or if we terminate our instructions due to one or more of circumstances (a)-(d) above or should the matter not be carried through to completion for some other reason, we will account to you on a time basis in respect of the work that has been carried out and for any disbursements and expenses that have been incurred.

Terms of Business

Your attention is drawn to the attached general terms of business that should be read in conjunction with this letter and which apply to this work. Please note that the attached terms of business form part of your contract with us. In the event of any conflict between a provision contained in this letter and a provision contained in the attached Terms of Business then the provision in this letter shall prevail.

Agreement

Please contact us if you require clarification of any points contained in this letter or the attached terms of business. You will be treated as having agreed to these terms unless we receive notice in writing from you to the contrary within ten working days of the date of this letter.

If at any time during the progress of this job you require any further information or assistance, please do not hesitate to let us know.

Yours faithfully

[Valuer's name]
[RICS Registered Valuer]
Fellow of the CAAV
For and on behalf of [   ]

t:
e:

Enc.   Terms of business
        Schedule of hourly rates

ANNEXE B

SAMPLE TEMPLATE FOR REPORT

NB For Valuers subject to the RICS Red Book, it is prudent to obtain an instruction from the client as to the format for the report, so excluding the presumptions of the Red Book that would otherwise apply.

This model report is intended to be just that: a help to members preparing their own agreements. The report will need to be tailored to suit necessary individual circumstances and sound local practices. The adaptation of this report to practical circumstances is a matter for the professional judgement of members for which the CAAV can accept no liability.

This template is drafted for valuations on the basis of the lower of cost and net realisable value. It would need to be revised where a valuation is to be on the basis of fair value.

Farm Stock Valuation
For Accounting Purposes
As at *(Insert Valuation Date)*
For
(Name of Client)

of

(insert address)

This report is the valuation for the purposes of annual accounts of the farm stocks held by .... in accordance with the terms of engagement dated .... and attached at Appendix 2. This report is to be read in conjunction with those terms of engagement.

Live and deadstock and harvested produce

	Number	**Class**	**Value £**
Cattle			
Sheep			
Deadstocks			
Harvested Produce			

Growing Crops and Acts of Cultivation

The cost of acts of cultivation, seeds, fertilisers and chemicals applied to the following crops:

Crop 1 – *(specify crop)*	**Area (ha)**	**Cost (£/ha)**	**Total**
Seeds			
Fertilisers			
Sprays			
Cultivations (incl. depreciation)			

Crop 2 – *(specify crop)*	Area (ha)	Cost (£/ha)	Total
Seeds			
Fertilisers			
Sprays			
Cultivations (incl. depreciation)			

Crop 3 – *(specify crop)*	Area (ha)	Cost (£/ha)	Total
Seeds			
Fertilisers			
Sprays			
Cultivations (incl. depreciation)			

Summary

	£
Cattle	
Sheep	
Deadstocks and Consumables	
Harvested Crops	
Growing Crops and Cultivations	
Total	

I estimate the value of the items enumerated in the foregoing inventory as at the valuation date in the sum of £ **(pounds).**
of which £   represents depreciation

This valuation is subject to the conditions and assumptions set out in Appendix 1.

Signed: ....   Date: [print date]
        [name of valuer]
        [RICS Registered Valuer]   Ref: [staff ref/job ref]
        For and on behalf of [   ]

                                      Doc ref:

APPENDIX

CONDITIONS AND ASSUMPTIONS APPLYING TO THE ATTACHED VALUATION

1 Purpose and Summary

This valuation has been prepared for stocktaking purposes and for incorporation in taxation accounts from information supplied by the client and our visit to the holding. It is prepared for accounting purposes only and should not be used in connection with any other purpose.

2 Technical Standards

This valuation has been carried out in accordance with:

(a) the Statement of Standard Accounting Practice 9 (SSAP 9) and HMRC Helpsheet HS232 "Farm Stock Valuation" (previously BEN 19) and had regard to the Central Association of Agricultural Valuers' "Guidance Notes on Agricultural Stock Valuations for Tax Purposes"

(b) [the current edition of RICS Valuation – Professional Standards].

3 Basis of Valuation, Valuation Approach and Definitions

3.1 Stocks have been valued at cost or, if lower, net realisable value.

3.2 Cost is defined as the expenditure incurred in the normal course of business in bringing the product to its present location and condition. The cost of cultivations and other operations, assessed using CAAV Costings as appropriate, includes depreciation unless specified otherwise.

3.3 Deemed Cost has been used where actual cost is not accurately ascertainable. Deemed cost is defined as:

Cattle   60% of market value
Sheep and pigs   75% of market value
Harvested crops   75% of market value

3.4 Net Realisable Value is defined as the actual or estimated selling price in the condition in which farmer intended to market it together with any grants or subsidies intended to augment that sale price and (for breeding/production animals) the ancillary stream of income from the sale of their progeny or produce less:

(a) all further costs to completion (including those for relevant progeny or produce); and

(b) all costs to be incurred in marketing, selling and distributing.

3.5 Market Value is defined as the estimated amount for which an asset should exchange on the date of valuation between a willing buyer and a willing seller in an arm's-length transaction after proper marketing wherein the parties had each acted knowledgeably, prudently and without compulsion.

3.6 Values based on net realisable value or market value have been ascertained by reference to market transactions at or around the valuation date.

3.7 No allowance has been made for any taxation liability (whether actual or notional) which may arise on the disposal of stock.

3.8 Other than as required by 3.4, no account has been taken of grants or subsidies.

4 Information Provided

The valuation has been based on the information supplied to us as to ownership, description, quantities and condition of stock items, and the valuation has been provided on the basis that this information is correct and that there are no undisclosed matters that would affect the valuation. We have not verified the legal ownership of any stocks nor verified quantities unless specifically requested to do so.

5 Extent of Investigations

Unless agreed otherwise we have carried out such investigations as we consider appropriate for the valuation including a brief inspection of such stocks as we consider appropriate for the valuation.

6 Assumptions

Unless stated otherwise, the following assumptions have been made in respect of stock items:

(a) That the assets are owned or contracted to be purchased by the client.
(b) That deadstocks are in useable condition.
(c) That livestock are in reasonable condition for their age.
(d) That growing crops are fully established and in reasonable condition for their growth stage.
(e) That harvested crops are fit for market.

7 Limitation of Liability

The valuation is provided for accounting / audit purposes only and may not be used for any other purpose. The valuation is for the sole use of the named client, is confidential to the client and his/her professional advisors and we do not accept any responsibility whatsoever to any other person in respect of the whole or any part of its contents. The valuation may not be used for loan security purposes.

8 Consent to Publication

Neither the whole nor any part of the valuation report or any reference thereto may be included in any document, circular or statement or published in any way without our prior written approval of the form and context in which it may appear, except that the information included herein may be used in published accounts of the client/business.

9 [   ] has undertaken previous stocktaking valuations for the client and has a continuing ongoing fee earning relationship with the client.

BIM33000 - Stock: meaning of: contents

BIM33015	What is stock
BIM33020	What is work in progress
BIM33025	What are long term contracts
BIM33030	Case law
BIM33035	A statutory definition of trading stock
BIM33040	What is stock when the trade includes hiring assets
BIM33045	What is stock when the trade includes hiring assets: factors to consider

BIM33100 - Stock: valuation: contents

The guidance in this chapter includes not only information on the acceptable valuation bases but also some descriptive paragraphs to give a feel for the important factors in a stock valuation. Stock valuation can never be absolutely precise, with a number of practical considerations affecting the accuracy of the estimate. SSAP9 provides the starting point for stock valuation for tax purposes, but you should note that it does not prohibit methods such as last in first out (LIFO) for costing stock. LIFO is **not** an allowable method for valuing stock for tax purposes.

There is extensive guidance on valuing farm stock in IR help sheet 232 - formerly BEN19.

BIM33110	Tax treatment of trading stock: Lord Nolan in Threlfall v Jones
BIM33115	The valuation bases
BIM33120	FIFO not LIFO: Minister of National Revenue v Anaconda American Brass Ltd
BIM33125	Non-allowable bases of valuation
BIM33130	Brief summary of SSAP9
BIM33132	International Accounting Standard 2 Inventories
BIM33135	Lower of cost and net realisable value: cost
BIM33140	Lower of cost and net realisable value: net realisable value
BIM33145	Net realisable value: use of formulae, slow moving stock, acceptable accuracy
BIM33150	Stock provisions
BIM33155	Valuing long term contracts
BIM33160	Mark to market or marking to market
BIM33165	Professional work-in-progress: general principles
BIM33170	Professional work-in-progress: chargeable staff and overheads
BIM33175	Professional work-in-progress: valuation: reduction to cost or net realisable value
BIM33180	Professional work-in-progress: valuation: payment uncertain
BIM33185	Professional work-in-progress: income recognition and debtors
BIM33190	Depreciation in stock
BIM33199	Change of accounting or tax basis of stock valuation

BIM55400 - Farming: stock valuation: contents

This chapter contains the following:

BIM55500 - Farming: herd basis: arrangement of guidance

This section contains the following:

ANNEXE D

Stock Valuations for Income Tax Purposes
Tax Bulletin May 1993
© Crown copyright

Reproduced with the permission of the Controller of Her Majesty's Stationery Office. Please note that each issue of the Bulletin contains certain qualifications which should be referred to before reliance is placed on an interpretation.

The Business Economics Note (BEN) on farm stock valuations for Income Tax purposes published in March 1993 should assist farmers and their professional advisers. It also applies, of course, for Corporation Tax.

We have been asked how we will deal with cases where a change in the basis of valuation is made as a result of the publication of the BEN.

The tax consequences of a change of basis should be negotiated by farmers and their Inspectors on the facts of the case concerned. The general principles followed by Inspectors are set out in SP3/90.

Paragraph 1 of the BEN explains that it supersedes all existing arrangements. This is because we consider that some existing practices of long standing are no longer acceptable. While those who have used such arrangements may have an expectation that they will continue, we cannot continue to operate practices which we do not think are correct. There are some particular situations where it may be helpful for you to know what guidance we have given to Inspectors.

These procedures are intended to make the transition to acceptable bases of valuation as smooth as possible. They are concerned with areas where particular aspects of the method of valuation are not acceptable for technical reasons. Nothing in what follows will inhibit Inspectors from examining critically cases where the quantity of stock has been materially understated or the valuations used are, technical issues apart, unacceptable.

Valuations on the basis of full rights and liabilities as at waygoing
We encouraged the use of full waygoing valuations in the 1940s when farmers were brought into Schedule D from Schedule B. Such valuations will include each of the three following elements:
- tillages and growing crops at a value which reflects the value of the crop rather than cost (ie including an element of profit);
- unexhausted manures;
- dilapidations based on a detailed survey.

Nowadays such valuations are usually prepared only on a change of tenant and the use for income tax purposes of valuations including all these elements is rare.

In 1957 we made it clear that such valuations were no longer acceptable for income tax purposes except in cases where they were already in use. Even so they may have been used in some cases which commenced after 1957. The new statement makes it clear that there are now no circumstances where this basis is acceptable.

If a change is made from a full waygoing basis to an acceptable basis on a normal accounting date before 30 June 1994 and the opening stock is recomputed on the same basis then Inspectors will not seek to adjust earlier years.

Other valuations including reserves for dilapidations
Such valuations are rare though more common than full waygoing valuations. The new statement makes it clear that they are not acceptable for income tax purposes. We have not previously made any general statement suggesting otherwise.

Where a change is made to an acceptable basis the opening stock for the year of change should be valued on the same basis as the closing stock. Our normal practice is to reopen earlier years and to seek interest and penalties where appropriate (paragraph 4 of SP3/90).

We accept, however, that there are cases where farmers have consistently included reasonable reserves. Where, in such cases, a change is made to an acceptable basis at a normal accounting date before 30 June 1994.

Inspectors will accept a current year adjustment without interest under Section 88 TMA 1970 or penalties computed as follows: —
* in cases where for tax purposes the trade began on or after 6 April 1987 the current year adjustment should be such that for tax purposes the valuation of the opening stock for the period of account of change is the same as the closing figure for the previous period. The effect is that no profits drop out of assessment:
* in other cases the adjustment should be computed by:

calculating the difference between the opening stock for the period of account of change on the new basis and the closing valuation of the previous period on the old basis, and deducting from it, the difference between the opening stock value on the new basis and the opening stock on the old basis on the date of commencement of the last period of account that ended before 6 April 1988. The effect is that the increase in the reserve arising since the start of the last accounting period ending before 6 April 1988 is taxed.

Reserves will be regarded as reasonable if they have been consistently included and do not exceed amounts which would have been included on waygoing. In other cases we will look as far back as many be considered appropriate on the facts of the case and seek interest and penalties where appropriate.

Tillages, unexhausted manures and growing crops
In 1942 we agreed with the NFU that, subject to the concurrence of the Appeal Commissioners:
* where the normal value of tillages, unexhausted manures and growing crops did not exceed £700 (later revised to £7000), and a detailed valuation was not available, a certificate that the value at the beginning of the year did not differ materially from that at the end of the year would usually be accepted, and
* even when the normal value exceeded £700 (£7000) a valuation would not be pressed for in every case and a similar certificate might be accepted after any enquiry necessary to establish its reasonable accuracy.

The use of such certificates is rare nowadays, but, in any event, this arrangement is no longer acceptable.

Where such certificates have been used consistently in the past and a change is made to an acceptable basis on a normal accounting date before 30 June 1994 and the opening stock is recomputed on the same basis we will not adjust earlier years.

Production animals where there is no normal market except for slaughter
Paragraph 3.3.3 of the BEN makes it clear that cull value is not an acceptable measure of net realisable value of animals kept for their produce and/or progeny. This is because the use of cull value only does not take account of the value of the income stream from the produce and/or progeny.

Paragraph 3.3.4 explains that we will accept writing down from cost to cull value over the productive life of the animal as a reasonable approximation of net realisable value for animals where there is no normal market except for slaughter at the end of their productive lives. Examples are breeding pigs (which are not usually sold except for slaughter because of possible disease problems of moving them to other herds) and laying hens (which are not usually sold except for slaughter because they stop laying if moved).

We wish to encourage the use of acceptable methods of valuation for production animals kept in these circumstances which are not part of a "herd basis" herd. Farmers who make the change from cull value with effect from a valuation date before 30 June 1994 may do so as follows:-
• cull value may continue to be used for animals which were on hand at the start of the year of change until the animal is sold; but
• acceptable methods should be used for animals acquired in the year of change or subsequently.

This will phase in the use of acceptable methods as animals in the production herd or flock are replaced.

After 30 June 1994 farmers who continue to use cull value only should be aware that what they are doing is not acceptable to the Inland Revenue and may be challenged in the normal way.

Unexhausted manures and dilapidations
The Central Association of Agricultural Valuers and the Royal Institution of Chartered Surveyors recommend that, in new cases, these items should be consigned to the balance sheet in the first accounts with no charge to profit and loss and not adjusted for in subsequent years. On cessation the difference between the closing and opening figures should be taken to profit and loss. We regard this method as acceptable if consistently used.

Factors which will not trigger investigation
A change to an acceptable basis made on a normal valuation date before 30 June 1994 from the use of
• full waygoing valuations;
• consistent inclusion of a reasonable dilapidations reserve;
• certificates prepared in accordance with the 1942 arrangement with the NFU; or
• valuation at cull value of production stock for which there is no normal market except for slaughter,
will not, of itself, be used as a reason for a general review of the reliability of the figures submitted. But of course, this will not preclude such an investigation if other aspects of the case are unsatisfactory.

ANNEXE E

SHORT ROTATION COPPICE

BIM55120 - Farming in Tax Law: Short Rotation Coppice
(NB This superseded the statement in the October 1995 Tax Bulletin)
© Crown copyright
Reproduced with the permission of the Controller of Her Majesty's Stationery Office.

Short rotation coppice consists of densely planted, high-yielding varieties of either willow or poplar, harvested on a 2 - 5 years cycle, although commonly every 3 years. The roots (or stools) are not disturbed and send up shoots, which are cut down to ground level and used for fuel.

ITA2007/S996 and FA95/S154 provides that the cultivation of short rotation coppice shall be treated as farming for Income Tax, Corporation Tax and Capital Gains Tax purposes and that the land occupied for such cultivation shall be agricultural land for inheritance tax purposes. The Act defines 'short rotation coppice' as 'a perennial crop of tree species planted at high density, the stems of which are harvested above ground level at intervals of less than ten years'.

COSTS OF PLANTING THE CUTTINGS

We regard the initial cultivation of the land including any spraying, ploughing, fencing and planting of the cuttings as capital costs. Any Woodland Grants received by the landowner should be matched with these capital costs.

CAPITAL GAINS TAX

The costs of planting the cuttings referred to in the previous paragraph represent expenditure on the land, as the stools form part of the land. They will be allowable (net of any grant offset against them) in computing chargeable gains if the land is disposed of, provided they are reflected in the state of the land at the time of disposal. The cost will not be allowable if the stools are grubbed up before the land is sold. If the capital costs are not incurred by the person in receipt of the Woodland Grant then this grant may give rise to a liability to capital gains tax.

The cost may be used to roll over gains from disposals of other business assets under HMRC ESC/D22 'Relief for the replacement of business assets: expenditure on improvements to existing assets'.

COSTS FOLLOWING THE PLANTING OF THE CUTTINGS

These costs are of two types:
• direct costs such as weeding, disease prevention, harvesting and the costs of the first cut (including labour and machinery costs), and
• indirect costs such as rent, maintenance of farm buildings and general management costs.

All these costs are revenue expenses and are allowable in full. Direct costs are allowed by matching them against subsequent receipts from the sale of the crop and up to that time we would expect to see them fully reflected in the annual valuation of the coppice as a crop or carried forward in some other way. If the coppice is cut in the first year to establish the stools any income from sale of the cut material should be offset against these expenses thus reducing the amount to be carried forward and allowed against the income from the first harvest. Indirect costs may be treated in the same way as direct costs. We regard this as preferable but in most cases deducting them in the general farming account rather than carrying them forward is acceptable. The principles are explained further in HMRC Business Economic Note 19 'Farming - Stock Valuation for Income Tax Purposes' (see BIM55410).

For subsequent cycles, the expenses of maintaining the crop should similarly be reflected in the valuation and matched against the receipts from the harvest. The anticipated biological life of the stools is around 30 years so approximately ten cycles may be expected.

SET ASIDE

Set aside payments received should be treated as farming income in the normal way. They are not regarded as income from the coppice since they would be received even if it was not grown.

COSTS AT THE END OF THE LIFE OF THE STOOL

Once the cycle of harvesting the coppice is over, the stools will normally be removed and, if necessary, drainage restored on the land. The costs incurred for the removal of the stools and their roots will be regarded as a capital expense. In view of the expected life of the stools these costs will be a long way off and a warning note must be sounded as law and practice may change. We regard the issues raised by short rotation coppice to be similar in principle to those relating to fruit orchards. At present a renewals allowance is available if orchards are replanted and HMRC would not seek to impose different treatment on the replacement of coppices. The costs of restoring drainage will be allowed as a revenue cost following HMRC SP5/81 'Expenditure on Farm Drainage'.

ANNEXE F

Treatment of the Single Payment

*CAAV Note – This is an extract from the Revenue's initial consolidated guidance on the
tax issues arising from the introduction of the Single Payment Scheme.*

Accountancy treatment

Following consultation with HMRC the Institute of Chartered Accountants of Scotland
and the Institute of Chartered Accountants in England and Wales have published
guidance for their members on accounting issues arising from the SPS. This has been
reproduced, with their permission, at Appendix 2. It explains the accounting principles
that need to be applied to the recognition of SP in farmers' accounts.

...

Farming: stock valuation: BEN 19

Following representations it has been decided not to revoke BEN 19, but to monitor its
relevance. However, it is worth noting that the SP, with the exception of the Scottish
Beef Calf Scheme (SBCS) is not linked to any particular crop, product or expense and
should not be taken into account in any calculation of the cost of stock. The SBCS
element should be accounted for in accordance with BIM55430.

Arable Area Payments
Tax Bulletin February 1994
© Crown copyright
Reproduced with the permission of the Controller of Her Majesty's Stationery Office. Please note that each issue of the Bulletin contains certain qualifications which should be referred to before reliance is placed on an interpretation.

CAAV Note – This article was written by the Inland Revenue in 1994. Its importance lies in its outline of the Revenue's approach to the treatment of grants of public money in stocktaking. This is then applied in the context of the old AAPS, still relevant to schemes such as the Protein Premium. The discussion of the then compulsory set-aside mechanism has been deleted from the Annexe.

The preceding article in the February 1993 Tax Bulletin on Payments under the Oilseeds Support Scheme 1992 has not been carried forward into this paper.

Support for arable farmers under the European Union's Common Agricultural Policy (CAP) was traditionally aimed at maintaining prices higher than world prices for sale of their crops. The reform of the arable regime in 1992 involved significant reductions in this kind of market-based support. To help compensate, farmers are now able to claim direct payments under the Amble Area Payments Scheme for the area of eligible crops which they grow.

Under the main scheme farmers can claim differing rates of area payments on cereals, oilseeds and proteins. In order to qualify, they must set aside part of the total area on which they are claiming. ....

All these payments are accepted as part of the trading income of farmers, and so it is not whether they are assessable but the time at which they should be recognised as income for tax purposes which is the subject of this article.

General approach to the recognition of grants
The time at which a grant that is revenue in character should be recognised for tax purposes is a complex area: some of the general principles are shown below.

Purpose
Although it is often difficult to identify the precise purpose of a grant, purpose is an important factor. It can show that it was intended that the grant should, for example, be set off against particular costs or be treated as a subsidy for a particular period. The purpose of a grant may be:
a. To subsidise trading income in general. In which case any amount of grant which is quantifiable with reasonable accuracy is a trading receipt for the period of account when the entitlement to the grant is established.
b. To meet particular costs. If so, it would be correct to match it with those costs and reduce them accordingly. If those costs are included in the closing stock valuation then the figure used should be the net costs after deducting the relevant grant.
c. To subsidise directly the sale proceeds. With such grants the correct treatment would be to recognise the grant as income in the year in which the crop is sold, consumed or abandoned. In this case the grants may have a material effect on the market value of stock for the purposes of the deemed cost method referred to at part 7 of Business Economic Note 19.

Entitlement

A grant should not be recognised for accounts purposes earlier than the point whe entitlement to it is established. Broadly the farmer becomes entitled when he or she ha fulfilled the material obligations required under the particular scheme, for example, b keeping an animal to the end of a specified retention period.

Quantification of Instalment Payments

Even when entitlement has been established the farmer may still have difficulty i quantifying what further instalments of grant he or she may reasonably expect to receiv later. Accounting practice can help. It provides that information available before th accounts are completed and signed should be taken into account in arriving at th quantification of the grant to which the farmer became entitled in the period of accoun concerned. Therefore, subject to any matching requirements under b and c above, wher entitlement is established within a period of account and the information available up t the date that the accounts are prepared allows further instalments (or the minimu amount of those instalments) to be quantified with reasonable accuracy, then th amounts should be recognised even if they were not received during the period c account. Otherwise, recognition may be deferred to the next period of account.

Treatment of Arable Area Payments

The Inland Revenue will accept accounts in which Arable Area Payments (including th required level of set-aside) are treated as a sales subsidy. On that basis the payments ar recognised as income for a particular accounting period to the extent that the crop ha been sold by the balance sheet date.

Where this approach is adopted and the rule of thumb described in Section 7 of Busines Economic Note 19 is used, valuations based on 75% of the total of the market value a the valuation date plus Arable Area Payments (including the required level of set-aside will be acceptable to Inspectors. Failure to take account of Arable Area Paymen (including the required level of set-aside) when computing deemed cost would result i the sum computed being too low by a material amount. The payments should also b taken into account when net realisable value is computed.

An example may be of assistance. The figures used are hypothetical and do not relate t any particular arable crop.

A farmer grows 85 hectares of an eligible arable crop and sets aside 15 hectares whic is the requirement for rotational set-aside. He accounts to 30 September by which tim the harvest of 500 tons has been gathered, half of it has been sold off the combine at £8 per ton and half is in store. The open market value of the crop in store at 30 Septembe is £90 per ton and stock is valued in accordance with the rule of thumb described i Section 7 of Business Economic Note 19. The farmer expects to receive Arable Are Payments of £200 per hectare for the crop and £300 per hectare for the set-aside lan making a total of £21,500 but it has not yet been paid. The accounts will include th following figures:

- Sales and Arable Area Payments   £32,750
  [250x £88 plus (1/2 x £21,500)]

- Stock (250 tons)   £24,937
  [75% x (250 x £90 plus (250 500 x £21,500))]

Straw has been ignored in computing these figures. This is acceptable to the Inland Revenue, though, of course, straw sales and stocks of straw must be included in the accounts.

Where accounts are prepared using a different recognition basis for Arable Area Payments, we will accept that basis provided that it reflects the correct application of generally accepted accounting practice, as interpreted by the Courts, to the particular facts and is consistently applied.

The Time at Which Animal Grants/Subsidies Should be Recognised for Tax Purposes
Tax Bulletin December 1994
© Crown copyright

Reproduced with the permission of the Controller of Her Majesty's Stationery Office Please note that each issue of the Bulletin contains certain qualifications which should be referred to before reliance is placed on an interpretation.

CAAV Note - This article was written by the Inland Revenue in 1994. It outlines the Revenue's approach to the treatment of livestock-based subsidies. It relies on the analysis in the paper on Arable payments. Other than for outstanding historic cases, may now only be relevant to the Scottish Beef Calf Scheme.

The general principles for dealing with timing issues relating to grants and subsidies were set out in the article on Arable Area Payments page 108 of Issue 10 of Tax Bulletin

That article did not comment on animal grants as, at that stage, we were awaiting accounting evidence.

We have now received representations from accountancy bodies about the correct time to recognise the following animal grants/subsidies:
• Suckler Cow Premium Scheme
• Beef Special Premium Scheme
• Sheep Annual Premium Scheme
• Hill Livestock Compensatory Allowances
• Extensification Payments

After considering those representations we accept that in most circumstances, correct accounting practice currently provides that it will be appropriate to recognise the grants listed above either:
• at the end of the retention period, or
• on receipt.

If either of these bases is consistently used in the accounts then Inspectors will accept that it is a valid basis for tax purposes.

Other bases may be recognised by accountancy bodies as reflecting the correct application of generally accepted accounting practice to the facts in particular cases. Inspectors will accept that such bases are valid provided they do not violate the taxing statutes as interpreted by the Courts. A change from the basis of recognition that is currently being used should only be made where the need to change outweighs the requirement that accounts should be produced on a consistent basis. Where such change is justified it will be dealt with in accordance with SP3/90, but practitioners should note that a change in accounting policy is one of the 'triggers' in the anti-avoidance proposal in connection with the transition to current year basis periods.

We are sometimes asked about the effect of animal grants/subsidies on valuations which are prepared on the basis of "deemed cost" as described in Section 7 of Business Economic Note 19. Where a grant/subsidy has been taken into account in full in

particular period then there is no effect on such valuations. Where a receipt has not been taken into account in a particular period but:
• the grant/subsidy has been applied for, and
• that application had a material effect on the market value of the animal,

then the grant should be taken into account as a supplement to the market value when deemed cost is computed.

Grants/subsidies which have been applied for but not recognised as income in the period concerned should also be taken into account in arriving at net realisable value for stock valuation purposes.

Bovine Spongiform Encephalopathy (BSE) and Farm Stocktaking Valuations
Inland Revenue Press Release 29th April 1996

*CAAV Note – This Revenue press release has been retained in this text not only again[st]
any major disruption of livestock trade in the future but also as an illustration of t[he]
Christmas Day issue – just because there is no trade on Christmas Day does not mea[n]
things have no value. In this case, when farmers retain livestock that cost them money [to]
keep, this may indicate that those animals have a value.*

Following discussions, the Inland Revenue today clarified the approach which applies [to]
the valuation of livestock for stock taking against the background of BSE. The need [to]
value stock at the end of March 1996 can be avoided by many taxpayers by t[he]
submission of a two year account covering the whole of the self assessment transiti[on]
period. In cases where a valuation is required the normal rules will continue to app[ly]
subject to a modification of the way in which market value is computed for cull cow[s,]
male calves born to dairy cows and beef cattle.

The Financial Secretary to the Treasury, Michael Jack, MP, said: "At this very difficu[lt]
time for farmers, I hope that this Inland Revenue announcement will be helpful [in]
removing one area of uncertainty, namely the approach to be adopted on stock valuatio[n]
in the BSE crisis. This approach has been agreed after contact with interested parties a[nd]
is to be welcomed."

DETAILS

1.   In calculating taxable profits from farming, like those from other businesses, [it]
is necessary to value trading stock at the annual date to which the accounts of t[he]
business are drawn up. This press release explains how the Inland Revenue will approa[ch]
the valuation of cattle in farm accounts at a date when markets are affected by publ[ic]
concern over BSE.

2.   Methods of valuation of farm stock for income tax and corporation tax purpos[es]
acceptable to the Inland Revenue are set out in Business Economic Note 19 (BEN1[9).]
This note was issued in March 1993 following consultation between the Inland Reven[ue]
and bodies representing farmers, landowners, agricultural valuers, accountants a[nd]
chartered surveyors.

3.   Many livestock farmers account to Lady Day (25 March) or 31 March and som[e]
to dates in April and May. In view of the limited and unsettled market in cattle followi[ng]
public concern over BSE, farmers and their professional advisers have been uncertain [as]
to how to value cattle at these year ends.

4.   In many cases the recent market conditions will affect valuations at the end [of]
the first of the two years which form the self assessment (SA) transition period. Farme[rs]
may prefer to prepare a two year account for the whole of their SA transition period th[us]
saving the need to value animals for income tax purposes at a time when the market [is]
unsettled. The Inland Revenue welcome this practice. However if a farmer wishes [to]
claim a loss for one of the years forming the basis of the SA transition period then [a]
separate account for that year will be needed.

5.   Until now the Inland Revenue have responded to queries from those who wish to prepare accounts by suggesting that they categorise and count the animals at the year end but await further guidance on how to value them. Following contact with representative bodies, the Inland Revenue are now able to give further guidance.

6.   Notwithstanding the market disruption caused by developments regarding BSE, the principles agreed between the Inland Revenue and representative bodies and set out in BEN19 will continue to apply to the valuation of livestock for stock taking.

7.   The main principle of stock valuation for income tax purpose, which is reflected in BEN 19, is that the valuation should reflect the cost of production or, if it is lower, the net realisable value of the stock.

8.   Where the farmer's records are not adequate to compute the cost of animals which are home bred or substantially home reared a percentage of market value can be used to arrive at a deemed cost of production. For cattle the percentage is 60 per cent. Deemed cost should not be used for purchased animals if it is less than the original purchase price plus, if the animal was immature when purchased, the costs of rearing from the date of purchase to the valuation date or, if earlier, to maturity.

9.   Public concern over BSE has considerably disrupted the normal markets for barren (or cull) cows, bull calves born to dairy cows and beef cattle. For animals in these categories there may be insufficient evidence to arrive at market value in the normal way because there was no market or only a very limited market at the valuation date. In such cases the Inland Revenue will accept that market value for the purposes of valuations in accordance with BEN19 may be taken as either
• the compensation subsequently paid on the slaughter of the animal, adjusted where necessary to reflect a change in weight between the accounting date and the date of slaughter or the compensation which would have been payable under the arrangements announced by the Government on April 16, by reference to the estimated weight of the animal at the accounting date, or
• the latest normal market value before 20 March 1996 less
    – 30 per cent for cull cows
    – 40 per cent for bull calves born to dairy cows
    – 20 per cent for beef cattle.

10.   A farmer may choose whether to estimate market value by using compensation value or the latest normal market value modified in accordance with the previous paragraph for animals in these categories but the same basis should be used for all the animals in any one of the three categories mentioned. Where deemed cost is used it will be 60 per cent of this figure.

11.   This arrangement may be applied for valuations at normal stocktaking dates between 20 March 1996 and 31 May 1996, both dates inclusive.

12.   Some people have suggested that stocktaking valuations of cattle at dates late in March 1996 at nil or nominal amounts can be used for tax purposes. This is not the Inland Revenue's view. Such figures would only be appropriate if at those dates there was evidence that sellers were not simply holding their animals back from market but rather were willing to dispose of them for at most nominal consideration. The Inland Revenue has not seen any evidence of such behaviour by sellers.

13.   Farmers remain at liberty, however, to value animals at net realisable val where there is no reasonable expectation that the eventual sale of the stock will cover costs. Guidance on the calculation of net realisable value is to be found in Busine Economic Note 19. Where under BEN 19 open market value at the valuation date m be used in arriving at net realisable value, farmers may use the method-described abo to work out for this purpose the open market value of barren cows, bull calves and be cattle.

THE HERD BASIS – EXTRACT FROM HMRC HELP SHEET 224

© Crown copyright

Reproduced with the permission of the Controller of Her Majesty's Stationery Office.

What is the herd basis?

The herd basis is a special method of calculating profits or losses which may be used by people who keep production livestock. If you use the herd basis you will need to keep records so that you can identify the figures to be used when applying the special rules.

As a normal rule, farm animals are dealt with as trading stock. However, some farm animals – those which are kept by farmers not primarily for resale but for the sake of the products (for example, milk or eggs) or offspring (for example, lambs or piglets) which they produce – are in many ways more like capital assets of the farmer's business. Tax law recognises this by giving farmers the option of dealing with such 'production animals' under the herd basis. It provides a set of rules whereby a herd or flock of production animals is excluded from trading stock and treated, in most but not all circumstances, like a capital asset.

A farmer must elect for the herd basis, otherwise the animals are treated as trading stock. The election must specify the class of animals concerned and, once it has been made, the herd basis must be used for as long as the farmer continues to keep animals of that class. The election has to be made soon after the farmer first starts keeping animals of that class, and then the herd basis applies to those animals from the outset. There is a further opportunity to elect to use the herd basis if a herd or a substantial part of it (20% or more) is compulsorily slaughtered.

What is the effect of electing for the herd basis?

Where a herd basis election is in force, the treatment for the purpose of computing farming profits of the herd or herds covered by the election is governed by the special rules. Very briefly they are:
- the initial cost of the herd is not an allowable deduction, nor is the cost of any subsequent increase in herd size
- the net cost of replacing animals in the herd (but not any element of improvement) is an allowable deduction
- where the odd animal, or just a few animals (amounting to less than 20% of the herd), are sold from the herd and not replaced, the resulting profit or loss is taken into account in arriving at the farming profits
- where the whole herd, or a substantial part (20% or more) of the herd, is sold and not replaced, the resulting profit or loss is not taken into account.

The herd basis can also apply where animals are jointly owned, for example, in some share-farming arrangements.

There are further special rules for particular situations.

Adjustments to be made in the Self-employment (full) pages of your personal tax return or the Partnership Tax Return

If you have made a herd basis election then you should include the herd in box 83 of your *Self-employment (full)* pages.

It may be helpful if you provide in the 'Any other information' box, box 102 breakdown of the figures showing the number and cost of the animals.

Similarly, you can use box 102 to explain any herd basis adjustments in your accoun or how you calculated the adjustments in boxes 59 to 61. Providing this information wi your tax return may help to avoid enquiries.

To get to the taxable profit, special adjustments may be needed to the profits shown k the accounts. This will depend upon the way the herd is accounted for. You should de with these adjustments by making entries in boxes 31 to 45 to remove profits or loss which have been included but which are not taxable, and/or expenses which have bee included but which are not allowable. If you have included a sum, which is not taxab in your business turnover, in box 14, then you should make the adjustment in box 61.

For example:
- an animal dies and is replaced by a better animal costing £200 more than a replaceme of the same quality as the one that died. Because of the way the accounts are prepare the cost of the replacement is included in box 16. The £200 which is not allowab should be included in box 31
- a substantial part of a herd is sold and the profit of £10,000 is included in box 28. It not taxable so it should be adjusted by a negative entry in box 43. If the profit had bee included in business turnover at box 14 then the adjustment would be made in box 6
- the following year the herd in the previous example is replaced. The cost of tl replacements is included in box 16. The proceeds of sale of the herd sold the previor year now become taxable and must be added to the profit. Make the adjustment in bc 59 and put a note in the 'Any other information' box, box 102 to explain the adjustme
- a home-bred dairy cow is added to a herd. The cost of breeding it is included in tl various expenses in the accounts. The farmer's records are inadequate to calculate tl cost accurately. The cost is estimated at 60% of market value (see Helpsheet 232 *Far and stock valuation*). If the sum to be disallowed has been included in sales, then r further adjustment is required. Otherwise the sum to be disallowed should be include in box 31.

If an adjustment is needed but you are not sure where to put it, please include it whe you think best and use the 'Any other information' box, box 102 to say what you hav done.

If you would like more information about the herd basis, ask us or your tax adviser.

ANNEXE K

Statement of Auditing Standards 520
Using the Work of an Expert
Reproduced with permission from the Auditing Practices Board

Covering Note - Statements of Auditing Standards ('SASs') are to be read in the light of 'The scope and the authority of APB pronouncements'. In particular, they contain basic principles and essential procedures ('Auditing Standards'), indicated by paragraphs in bold type, with which auditors are required to comply in the conduct of any audit. SASs also include explanatory and other material which is designed to assist auditors in interpreting and applying Auditing Standards. The definitions in the Glossary of terms are to be applied in the interpretation of SASs.

Introduction
1.   The purpose of this SAS is to establish standards and provide guidance on using the work of an expert to obtain audit evidence. Auditors have sole responsibility for their opinion, but may use the work of an expert. Such an expert may be engaged by an entity to provide specialist advice on a particular matter which affects the financial statements or by auditors in order to obtain sufficient appropriate audit evidence regarding certain financial statement assertions.

2.   When using the work performed by an expert, auditors should obtain sufficient appropriate audit evidence that such work is adequate for the purposes of the audit. (SAS 520.1)

3.   'Expert' means a person or firm possessing special skill, knowledge and experience in a particular field other than auditing.

4.   The auditors' education and experience enable them to be knowledgeable about business matters in general, but they are not expected to have the expertise of a person trained for, or qualified to engage in, the practice of another profession or occupation.

5.   An expert may be engaged by the entity or the auditors. The expert may also be employed by the entity or the auditors.

6.   When auditors use the work of an expert employed by them or by an associated firm, that work is used in the employee's capacity as an assistant on the audit as contemplated in SAS 240 'Quality control for audit work'. Accordingly, in such circumstances the requirements of SAS 240 apply as well as those of this SAS.

Determining the need to use the work of an expert
7.   During the audit the auditors may obtain, in conjunction with the entity or independently, audit evidence in the form of reports, opinions, valuations or statements of an expert.

Examples are:
* valuations of certain types of assets, for example land and buildings, plant and machinery, works of art, precious stones, unquoted investments and intangible assets:
* determination of quantities or physical condition of assets, for example minerals stored in stockpiles, underground mineral and petroleum reserves and the remaining useful life of plant and machinery;

- determination of amounts using specialised techniques or methods, for example pe sions accounting and actuarial valuations;
- the measurement of work completed and to be completed on contracts in progress; ai
- legal opinions concerning interpretations of agreements, statutes and regulations, or c the outcome of litigation or disputes.

8.   When determining whether to use the work of an expert, the auditors review:
     (a) the importance of the matter being considered in the context of the financi statements;
     (b) the risk of misstatement based on the nature and complexity of the matt being considered; and -
     (c) the quantity and quality of other available relevant audit evidence.

9.   If the auditors determine that it is appropriate to seek to use the work of ɛ expert, the approach is discussed and may be agreed with management or the directoɪ If management or the directors are unable or unwilling to engage an expert, the audito may consider engaging an expert or whether sufficient appropriate audit evidence can I obtained from other sources. If unable to obtain sufficient appropriate audit evidenc they consider the implications for their report.

Competence and objectivity of the expert
10 When planning to use the work of an expert the auditors should assess the obje tivity and professional qualifications, experience and resources of the expert. (SA 520.2)

11.   Normally, this involves considering the expert's:
     (a) professional certification, or licensing by, or membership of, an appropria professional body; and
     (b) experience and reputation in the field in which the auditors are seeking auɔ evidence.

12.   The risk that an expert's objectivity is impaired increases when the expert is:
     (a) employed by the entity; or
     (b) related in some other manner to the entity, for example by being financial dependent upon, or having an investment in, the entity.

13.   If the auditors are concerned about the competence or objectivity of the expɛ they may discuss their reservations with management or the directors and consid whether sufficient appropriate audit evidence can be obtained. They may undertaⅠ additional audit procedures or seek evidence from another expert. If unable to obta sufficient appropriate audit evidence, they consider the implications for their report.

The expert's scope of work
14.   The auditors should obtain sufficient appropriate audit evidence that tl expert's scope of work is adequate for the purposes of their audit. (SAS 520.3)

15.   Audit evidence may be obtained through a review of the items of referenc which are often set out in written instructions from the entity to the expert. Suɛ instructions to the expert may cover such matters as:
- the objectives and scope of the expert's work;
- a general outline as to the specific matters the expert's report is to cover;
- the intended use of the expert's work, including the possible communication to thɪ parties of the expert's identity and extent of involvement;

- the extent of the expert's access to appropriate records and files; and
- information regarding the assumptions and methods intended to be used by the expert and their consistency with those used in prior periods.

In the event that these matters are not clearly set out in written instructions to the expert, the auditors may seek to communicate with the expert directly to obtain audit evidence in this regard.

Assessing the work of the expert

16.   The auditors should assess the appropriateness of the expert's work as audit evidence regarding the financial statement assertions being considered. (SAS 520.4)

17.   This involves assessment of whether the substance of the expert's findings is properly reflected in the financial statements or supports the financial statement assertions, and consideration of:
- the source data used;
- the assumptions and methods used;
- when the expert carried out the work;
- the reasons for any changes in assumptions and methods compared with those used in the prior period; and
- the results of the expert's work in the light of the auditors' overall knowledge of the business and the results of other audit procedures.

18.   When considering whether the expert has used source data which is appropriate in the circumstances, the auditors may consider the following procedures;
      (a) making enquiries regarding any procedures undertaken by the expert to establish whether the source data is sufficient, relevant and reliable; and
      (b) reviewing or testing the data used by the expert.

19.   The appropriateness and reasonableness of assumptions and methods used and their application are the responsibility of the expert. The auditors do not have the same expertise and, therefore, cannot necessarily challenge the expert's assumptions and methods. However, they seek to obtain an understanding of the assumptions and methods used and to consider whether they are reasonable, based on their knowledge of the business and the results of other audit procedures, and compatible with those used for the preparation of the financial statements.

20.   If the results of the expert's work are not consistent with other audit evidence, the auditors attempt to resolve the inconsistency by discussions with the entity and the expert. Applying additional procedures, including possibly engaging another expert, may also assist in resolving the inconsistency.

21.   If the auditors are not satisfied that the work of an expert provides sufficient appropriate audit evidence and there is no satisfactory alternative source of such evidence, they consider the implications for their report.

22.   When the auditors are satisfied that the work of an expert provides appropriate audit evidence, reference is not made to the work of the expert in their report. Such a reference may be misunderstood and interpreted as a qualification of the auditors' opinion or a division of responsibility, neither of which is appropriate.

Compliance with International Standards on Auditing

23.   Compliance with this SAS ensures compliance in all material respects wi International Standard on Auditing 620 'Using the Work of an Expert'.

Effective data

24.   Auditors are required to comply with the Auditing Standards contained in th SAS in respect of audits of financial statements for periods ending on or after ? December 1995.

ANNEXE L

Schedule of HMRC Guidance, Statutes and Cases

Legislation
Regulation (EC) 1606/2002 on the application of international accounting standards

Income and Corporation Taxes Act 1988
Finance Act 2005
Income Tax (Trading and Other Income) Act 2005 (ITTOIA)
Companies Act 2006
Corporation Tax Act 2009

HMRC Guidance
Business Income Manual (permanently subject to review) – current contents at Annexe C
Help Sheet IR 232 (previously BEN 19) (March 1993) – See Chapter 3 above
Tax Bulletin (May 1993) – Stock Valuations for Income Tax Purposes (Annexe D above)
Tax Bulletin (February 1994) Arable Area Payments (Annexe G above)
Tax Bulletin (December 1994) – The Time at Which Animal Grants/Subsidies Should be
    Recognised for Tax Purposes (Annexe H above)
Tax Bulletin (October 1995 as replaced by BIM 55120) (Annexe E above)
Inland Revenue Press Release 29th April 1996 – Bovine Spongiform Encephalopathy
    (BSE) and Farm Stocktaking Valuations (Annex I)
Tax Bulletin Special Edition (June 2005) – Treatment of the Single Payment (Annex F
    above)
Help Sheet HS224 (2012) – Extract on Herd Basis at Annexe J above

Cases
CIR v Cock Russell & Co [1949] 29 TC 387
Gallaher v Jones [1993] 66 TC 77; [1994] Ch 107
HMRC v William Grant & Sons Distillers Ltd [2007] UKHL 15 on appeal from [2005]
    EWHC 553 (Ch)
Johnston v Britannia Airways Ltd [1994] 67 TC 99
Ostime v Duple Motor Bodies Ltd [1961] 39TC537 1WLR739
Small v Mars UK Ltd [2007] UKHL 15 on appeal from [2005] EWHC 553 (Ch)
Threlfall v Jones [1993] 66 TC 77
Whimster and Co v CIR [1925] 12 TC 813

Accountancy Publications
SSAP 2
SSAP 9
FRS 17

IAS 2 - Inventories
IAS 41 – Agriculture
IFRS for SMEs (July 2009) – Section 34 on Agriculture Statement of Auditing Standards
    520 - Using the Work of an Expert (1995) (Annexe K above)

.